The Donner Party

Weathering the Storm

MARK
McLAUGHLIN
Oct. 20, 2009

First Printing 2007
Second Printing 2007, revised

Cover design and layout by *Riley Works*, Springfield, OR

Printed and bound in the United States of America

Library of Congress Control Number: 2006906081

ISBN: 0-9657202-5-X

Mic Mac Publishing

P. O. Box 483 • Carnelian Bay, CA 96140
<www.MicMacMedia.com>

Contents

Acknowledgments

This book is an excerpt from my Weather History of the Sierra Nevada project, which has been a work in progress for nearly two decades. Over the years, many people have encouraged my efforts to write about the weather history of this dynamic region. The folks listed below were especially helpful with this book.

Kristin Johnson, the noted Donner Party expert, author and historian, spent considerable time and care reviewing the draft of this book, and her critical eye for detail greatly improved the veracity of this complicated story. Johnson deserves much credit for her dedication to dispelling many of the myths, legends and contradictions of this famous western saga.

I want to thank **Steve Beck**, archivist at Sutter's Fort State Historic Park, for his friendly, open door policy. He graciously allowed me to explore the Sutter's Fort archives to fulfill my extensive wish list of images to use in illustrating this book.

Randall Osterhuber, lead scientist at the Central Sierra Snow Laboratory near Donner Pass, provided me with the Sierra snowfall chart and several of his own personal photographs depicting severe conditions during heavy winters on the summit.

My parents, *John and Florence McLaughlin*, were very helpful in reviewing the manuscript for typographical and grammatical errors, as well as pointing out where I had "lost the trail" in the narrative.

Archaeologist **Susan Lindstrom** told me about tree ring studies that had been done years ago, and pointed me to University of Nevada - Reno anthropologist Donald Hardesty who generously shared the climate reconstruction data with me.

Over the years, many weather experts have gladly assisted with my research efforts — especially *John James, Hal Klieforth and Jim Goodridge*.

Special thanks to professional photographers, *Richard Steinheimer and Shirley Burman*, for giving me permission to publish a few of their images taken during the epic winter of 1983.

Dohn Riley, of Riley Works (www.rileyworks.com), Springfield, Oregon, for his critical eye; both in format and text.

Frank Mullen, author of *The Donner Party Chronicles* and senior reporter at the *Reno Gazette-Journal*, discussed with me some of the details and source material for determining how deep the snow actually was at Donner Lake during the winter of 1847.

Donner descendant *Lochie Paige* graciously invited me to the 2006 Donner Family Reunion Picnic at Donner Lake where I enjoyed lunch with some of the extended family members in attendance. Their family pride in their ancestor's western legacy is commendable and honorable.

I'm grateful for the inspiration of *David Ludlum* (1910 – 1997), America's first and foremost weather historian. After his retirement in 1994, Ludlum generously gave me all of his California weather history files to aid in my own research efforts.

Special thanks to *Nora O'Neill*, my wife and partner, who has always supported my professional career with enthusiasm and love.

Introduction

THIS BOOK PRESENTS A FRESH LOOK at the Donner Party experience, a classic pioneer survival story told with a new, unique weather perspective. Hundreds of articles and dozens of books have been written about the 1846 Donner party, but this is the first to chronicle the dramatic events as they developed with each blizzard and winter storm.

The members of the ill-fated Donner party didn't know it at the time, but severe weather during the second half of October 1846 had buried the upper elevations of the Sierra Nevada and blocked the principal mountain pass to northern California. Unseasonably early winter storms that year had dumped six feet of snow on the 7,000-foot-high mountain pass the pioneers must cross to reach the safety of Sutter's Fort in California. The deep snow effectively stranded the late-arriving emigrants east of the Sierra crest where they were snowbound for a winter without adequate provisions and shelter.

The Donner party consisted of a handful of families with many children, as well as single men hired as teamsters to maintain wagons and livestock. Other members had joined the wagon train later for safety and strength in numbers as they all struggled west toward a better life in California. There were German, Irish and English immigrants; Protestants, Catholics and Mormons. Some were virtually penniless while others had plenty of money to buy property and build a nice home. Most were middle-class Americans, but nearly half were children under the age of eighteen.

It was October and many of the people in the Donner party had been on the trail for nearly half a year; a tough strenuous trek through steep, rugged mountains and parched, searing deserts. The group was running behind schedule, but they were hopeful that winter weather might hold off for just a couple more weeks. The two previous winters in the Sierra Nevada had been relatively dry; the year before snow didn't close the pass until the end of December. Unfortunately, the odds were stacked against the Donner party; it was only a matter of time before an early winter would catch a late-arriving wagon train.

As October 1846 drew to a close and the determined emigrants approached their final hurdle, Truckee Pass (later re-named Donner), it had to be beyond their collective imagination that they were about to spend another four to five months isolated in these mountains, pushed to the limits of human endurance, and beyond. Ultimately, 36 of the 81 people trapped in the mountains died from starvation, exposure and fatigue.

It is by far the most tragic weather event ever in the Sierra Nevada. The California-bound Donner party did not arrive in the Truckee Meadows (near present-day Reno, Nevada) until October 20, 1846. After a rest of six days the vanguard of these trail-weary emigrants struggled up to Truckee Lake (Donner Lake), which they reached on October 31. On the way Captain George Donner injured his hand repairing a wagon and was forced to encamp about five miles north of the lake. During this push west, the second heavy snowfall of the season enveloped the higher elevations.

October snow is not unusual in the Sierra (50 inches fell at the Central Sierra Snow Lab near Donner Pass during the second half of October 2004), but the coincidence of two storms heavy enough to impede traffic at this early date are rare. There were about 10 major storm periods during the winter of 1847 beginning October 16, 1846, and ending in early April 1847. All of them added materially to the season's remarkable accumulation, but it was the late October and early November snowfalls that blockaded the trans-Sierra route for the Donner party.

In early November, a series of storms lasting eight days pounded the mountains with rain and snow. When the skies finally cleared on November 13, the snow was about ten feet deep at elevations above 7,000 feet. Although fair weather for the next two weeks melted most of the snow around Donner Lake, and settled the summit snow pack to six feet, intense arguments and well-grounded fear stymied a breakout to safety. They reluctantly realized that the ascent over Donner Pass was just the beginning of the journey over the Sierra Nevada hump. Another powerful series of storms at the end of November dumped about five feet of snow at Donner Lake (even more in the high country), which sealed the fate for the luckless emigrants.

While the pioneers anxiously awaited the arrival of rescue efforts from the Sacramento Valley, powerful Pacific storm systems continued to hit the mountains. Hard as the relentless blizzards were to take, physically and mentally, the sunshine and thaws during the intervening periods of fair weather gave rise to false hopes that the deadly winter pattern would break soon.

More snow in December dimmed their expectations and increased the snow depth at the lake to seven feet, with double that amount on the summit. Mid-month, a lull in storm activity encouraged 15 of the party to attempt a desperate crossing on homemade snowshoes. Each member of the "Forlorn Hope" carried about a week's supply of starvation rations. It took them 33 days to reach the first settlement, Johnson's Ranch in the Sacramento Valley. Only seven of the snowshoers survived their horrific ordeal of fatigue, starvation and cannibalism, including all five women who set out.

During a mid-February interlude of fair weather, two rescue parties from California succeeded in crossing the mountains to reach the snow-bound encampments. One group of seven able-bodied men escorted 17 starving people (many of them children) out of the mountains beginning on March 3. While making their way to safety, they were blasted by a severe blizzard that lasted two days. Many members of this group, which included all nine members of the Breen family, were too weak to go on. They built a fire and desperately waited for help. Their campfire melted the snow pack until they were huddled in a pit 24 feet deep. A rescue party found them four days later. More snow fell in March with the final major storm period lasting from March 28 to April 3. Louis Keseberg, the last remaining survivor, was rescued from Donner Lake on April 20.

The tale of the Donner party is complex, complicated and convoluted. This book can not attempt to tell the complete story with its countless details and unsolved mysteries — there are other books to fill in the blanks — but it does provide an accurate, entertaining, and riveting account of the West's most infamous storm story.

Enjoy.

Dedication

To Ann Houghton Smith, who died January 26, 2006, just six days shy of her 82nd birthday. She was the granddaughter of Sherman O. Houghton and Eliza P. Donner, and great granddaughter of Tamsen Donner. I first met Ann Smith during the sesqui-centennial celebration of the 1846 pioneer migra-tion held in Reno, Ne-vada, in 1996. Friendly and helpful, Ann always treated me with great kindness and I appreci-ated her sense of humor and cheerful generosity.

Mark and Ann in September 2000

In 1994, Ann released a valuable family collection of Donner memorabilia including artifacts, news clippings, photographs, and correspondence. She also shared revealing letters written by Tamsen to her sister Elizabeth Eustis during the 1820s and 1830s. The collection was considered one of the most important to surface in fifty years.

Among its many inaccuracies, this rare 1826 map of the West is missing the Sierra Nevada range. For that reason, rivers draining the west slope of the Rocky Mountains flow all the way to the Pacific Ocean. This misconception inspired John Bidwell, a 21-year-old, California-bound schoolteacher, to lead a wagon train toward the Great Salt Lake in 1841. On his map, the mythical Buenaventura River drained from the lake westward, all the way to the Bay of San Francisco. Bidwell hoped to convert their wagons to boats in order to run the river to California. The Bidwell Party eventually succeeded in reaching Sutter's Fort (Sacramento) via the Humboldt River, which flows west across present-day Northern Nevada.

By 1846, emigrants knew that they had to cross the "California Mountains" to reach Sutter's Fort, but contemporary maps were still lacking many of the physical features we associate with the Great Basin. John Frémont, an officer in the Army Corps of Topographical Engineers, first explored and mapped the region in 1843 –1845, but pioneers in 1846 were still relying on guidebooks by California land promoters like Lansford W. Hastings for much of their information. Although most of the Great Basin region was still terra incognito, by 1846, wagon companies heading to California were confident enough in the trail that they felt no need to hire mountain men as guides to get them through. The California Trail was well mapped by the start of the Gold Rush in 1849.

Credit: The Beinecke Rare Book and Manuscript Library, Yale University

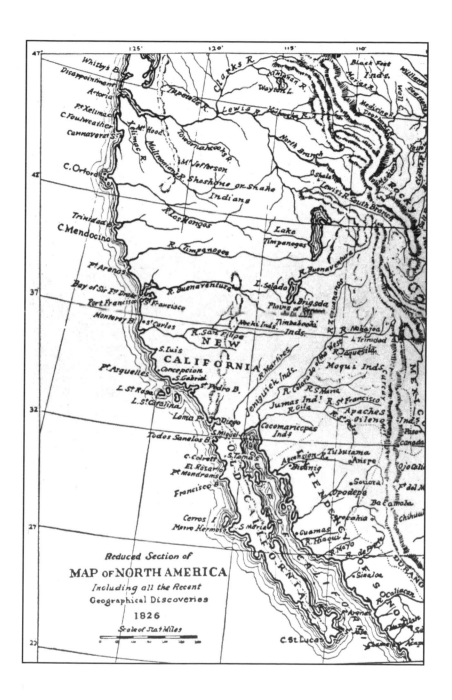

Reduced Section of
MAP OF NORTH AMERICA
Including all the Recent
Geographical Discoveries
1826
Scale of Stat Miles

xi

October 1846:
First Snow

1

DONNER PASS & SIERRA NEVADA

In early October 1846, one of the last westbound wagon trains of that year's emigration to California was crossing the 7,000-feet-high Truckee Pass (later re-named Donner Pass). Like hundreds of other pioneers, James Mathers had endured countless challenges during his 2,000-mile overland trek, but the arduous climb over the Sierra Nevada was the hardest of all. Mathers tackled the high Sierra pass on October 6 and reached Summit Valley the next day.

In the years before the California gold rush, most emigrants departed from the mid-west in late March or early April, usually crossing the Missouri River in early May. The wagon trains traveled through Fort Kearny (Nebraska) and Fort Laramie (Wyoming) during late spring, averaging from 15 to 25 miles per day. The trip was timed to take advantage of the abundant grass in spring and summer, and to avoid late fall or early winter storms in the West. The first pioneers usually started arriving at Sutter's Fort (California) by early September, well before the approach of California's wet winter season.

Emigrant guidebooks had warned that it was important to cross the California Mountains as early as possible and Mathers could see why. It was only October 7, but he wrote in his journal; "The weather was cold and we had frequent squalls of snow…" A couple of days later the early season storm had cleared out, but there was still a brisk chill in the high country. James Mathers probably wondered about the safety of other people farther behind his company, which included the wagon train captained by George Donner.

A week later bad weather once again swept in from the Pacific Ocean and the last pioneers to make it out of the mountains had disturbing news. Samuel Young, who had crossed the pass on October 16, said that snow had been falling there "at a fearful rate" and they had lost one of their wagons when it crashed into an abyss. George Tucker, who had traveled with the Smith Company behind the Donner party until they reached Fort Bridger and then went ahead with a faster group, confirmed that conditions in the mountains were quickly deteriorating: "The day after we left Bear Valley it commenced raining which I think was about the 18th of October. The next day we could see the snow on the mountains behind us. We knew the Donner Company would have trouble." (Tucker would later play a key roll in the rescue operations.) The Donner party, still miles east of the pass, had no idea that the terrible winter of 1847 was already underway.

CALIFORNIA COAST

It was mid-afternoon on October 15, 1846, but when Dr. Marius Duvall gazed east from the deck of the *U.S.S. Congress*, he could see nothing of the rugged California coast he knew was just a few miles away. Despite wearing a heavy coat, he shivered as he wrote in his journal "thick misty weather and cold." Three days later, when the *Congress* was anchored in Monterey Bay, Dr. Duvall observed; "The weather thick and calm, exerting a depressing influence upon one's spirits."

The *Congress*, an American flagship under the command of Commodore Robert Stockton, was sailing from San Francisco Bay to Monterey in preparation for military action along the southern California coast. A fleet of U. S. warships had been patrolling the ports and harbors of California ever since the breakout of the Mexican-American War about six months before.

Dr. Duvall, a United States Navy Assistant Surgeon, was assigned to several different vessels, including the *U.S.S. Savannah* and the sloop-of-war *U.S.S. Portsmouth*. As part of his daily duties, Dr. Duvall kept a journal of his travels up and down the coast of California and Mexico. He often jotted down weather conditions, specifically focusing on wind speed and direction. The month of October is normally the end of California's dry season, but in 1846, Dr. Duvall noted early winter rains had turned the coastal countryside a "spring green." It was an auspicious start to a fateful winter.

Edwin Bryant, one of the first overland pioneers to arrive in California that year, was safe in Sonoma, but on October 17 he noted, "The last two mornings have been cloudy and cool. The rainy season, it is thought by the weather-wise in this climate, will set in earlier this year than usual. The periodical rains ordinarily commence about the middle of November. It is now a month earlier, and the meteorological phenomena portend 'falling weather.'"

Snow covered Sierra Nevada west slope. Photo by Mark McLaughlin

DONNER PARTY — ON THE TRAIL

The members of the Donner party had already endured more than their fair share of bad luck, poor decisions and organizational collapse. Unfortunately, the worst was yet to come. Comprised of families with young children, single men hired as teamsters to maintain wagons and livestock, and an assortment of late comers, the Donner party would endure much more suffering and death over the next four months.

The westbound emigrants did not reach the Truckee Meadows (near present-day Reno, Nevada) until about October 20. (Some dates associated with the Donner Party are approximate.) The skies were cloudy and the mountains ahead were already white with the season's first snowfall. Worst yet, another storm was brewing. Years later, John Breen recalled his memories of the weather as the Donner wagon train traveled up the Truckee River: "There began to be heavy clouds on the high range of mountains to the west, and this from what we had learned from Captain Frémont was a certain sign of snow on the mountains." Over the next few days, rain developed with snowfall in the upper elevations.

Down along the California coast and in the Sacramento Valley, the next storm had moved onshore. While enroute in a boat from Sonoma to Yerba Buena (San Francisco), Edwin Bryant noted, "The damp raw weather, auguring the near approach of the autumnal rains, continues. A drizzling mist fell on us during the night, and the clouds were not dissipated when we resumed our voyage this morning."

As he approached Sutter's Fort and the end of his long journey, James Mathers wrote that the weather there was cloudy and cool.

A much more powerful winter storm slammed into the mountains during the evening of October 28. James Reed arrived at Sutter's Fort just before the rain began — rain that turned to snow in the mountains where his family struggled up the steep slope of the Sierra Nevada. Reed had stabbed to death teamster John Snyder along the Humboldt River during a fight. He was banished from the wagon train as a result, which gave him the opportunity to ride ahead to California to acquire provisions from John Sutter. Two other members of the Donner party, Charles Stanton and William McCutchen, had already left the company before the murder to get help at Sutter's Fort. McCutchen fell ill once they arrived at the fort, but Stanton was able to procure seven mules laden with supplies from Sutter and "borrowed" two American Indians, Luis and Salvador, to act as guides for the struggling wagon train. Maintaining a brisk pace, Stanton, Luis, and Salvador made it over the pass before the snow became too deep.

While descending the Sierra west slope into California, Reed had passed the eastbound Stanton and told him that he would be following close behind with more provisions.

Bear Valley on Sierra west slope. Photo by Mark McLaughlin

James Reed was very determined; after all, his wife and four children were still back on the trail with the others, but this third October snowstorm would stymie his valiant efforts to return to his family.

At Sutter's Fort the rain fell heavily and steadily for about 12 hours, with the clouds clearing out during the afternoon of October 29. Edwin Bryant reported that when the storm ended, the weather and temperature "were delightful." The rain was over in the valley, but the respite would be brief. A long rainy period would soon set in on the evening of October 31.

Onboard the *U.S.S. Portsmouth*, which was anchored in Monterey Bay, the morning weather observer on October 29 noted in the ship's deck log that the barometric pressure was falling, and the winds moderate from the southwest with heavy rains. The sun came out again on the 30th, but by the following day the *Portsmouth* was again reporting southwest winds with clouds and rain.

Fifty inches of snow fell on Donner Pass in October 2004. Photo by Mark McLaughlin

The wet weather was even having an effect on the American military's efforts to defeat the Mexican army. On October 31, *The Californian* newspaper reported "Last account from General Taylor he was in Monterey with 5,000 men, intended not to advance farther south on account of the rains."

View of Donner Lake looking east from Donner Pass. Photo by Mark McLaughlin

In the mountains, however, weather conditions were much more serious. Snow was beginning to accumulate on the trail east of the Sierra crest as the Donner party hurried along as best they could through the Alder Creek Valley. In their rush to reach the pass, the emigrants had split into three groups as some traveled faster than others. The Donner families had fallen behind the other emigrants who reached Donner Lake by the end of the month. Years later pioneer William C. Graves remembered: "On the 30th of October 1846, we camped in a pretty little valley about five miles from Donner Lake; that night it snowed about eight inches deep."

First snow on Alder Creek Valley. Photo by Mark McLaughlin

At the end of October, the vanguard of the wagon train moved out quickly and hurried along the north shore of Donner Lake toward the summit. They wanted to reach the pass as soon as possible before another storm closed it for good, but they were already too late. Patrick Breen, one of the pioneers in the lead, later recounted their futile attempts to cross the summit and that the snow on Donner Pass was so deep that they could not find the road.

William Graves said the same thing: "We got about four miles past the lower end of the lake, but could not go any further because the snow was about four feet deep. We were within one mile of the top, when some were obliged to give it up and go back to the lake." The pioneers were actually fortunate that they did not succeed in crossing the summit because an extended storm period was just about to set in and the conditions in the high country west of Donner Pass would be much worse than at Donner Lake.

Californian historian Hubert H. Bancroft later wrote: "They reached the eastern base of the Sierra, which loomed before them high into the heavens, a white wall glistening with frosted pines. Climbing upward as far as they could go, they found the top of Truckee pass five feet under snow." For a historian, Bancroft certainly wrote with a flourish: "They ascended to within three miles of the summit, where they now found ten feet of snow, each moment thickened by the clouds. It was very cold. The wind howled round the crags, and the whirling snow blinded, and every moment threatened to engulf them. They saw how impossible it was to proceed farther, so returning to the cabin, they made preparations to winter there, near what is now called Donner Lake." (The cabin was built by members of the Stephens Party in 1844.)

SACRAMENTO VALLEY

Meanwhile, down at Sutter's Fort, James Reed was anxious to return to the mountains to help rescue his family and friends. By now, William McCutchen had regained his strength and was also ready to help. Unfortunately, it was too late for ev-

Donner Party caught in early season snowstorm.

eryone concerned. Reed later described his attempt to cross the mountains: "The second night [Oct. 30] after my arrival at Captain Sutter's, we had light rain; next morning we could see snow on the mountains. The Captain stated that it was low down and heavy for the first fall of the season. The next day I started on my return with what horses and saddles Capt. Sutter had to spare..." Despite Sutter's warnings that it would be impossible to traverse the mountains, Reed and McCutchen headed east toward the high country.

James Frazier Reed. Courtesy California State Parks. Sutter's Fort Archives

The late October storm in 1846 was cold enough to cover the lower elevations east of the pass with a few inches of snow, enough to slow the progress of the rear guard of settlers that included the two Donner families. After one of George Donner's wagons broke an axle and flipped over, they were forced to stop for repairs in Alder Creek Valley. The Donners and their hired teamsters were now stuck at Alder Creek while the lead members of the wagon train were getting ready to build "temporary quarters" at the lake.

November 1846: Trapped

2

ALDER CREEK VALLEY

The Alder Creek encampment, located about five miles northeast of Donner Lake, was a hectic scene during the early days of November 1846. The two Donner families and their hired help were bogged down by snow, injury and fatigue, and separated from the main group, some of whom had reached Donner Lake by the end of October. The Donners decided to make camp in a protected grove at the junction of Alder and Prosser creeks.

The Alder Creek Valley has relatively flat, open meadows surrounded by stands of pine. The Alder Creek drainage provides enough water to support dense moisture-loving thickets of mountain alder. The valley's elevation is about 5,800 feet above sea level with an average snowfall of 13.5 feet each winter. Situated farther east away from the Sierra crest, the Alder Creek Valley receives less snow than Donner Lake or the pass, but the pioneers trapped there couldn't have been very optimistic about their prospects.

The trouble at Alder Creek started when one of Captain George Donner's wagons broke an axle and crashed on a steep hill. Later that day George was wounded when the ax his brother Jake was using to carve a piece of wood into a replacement axle glanced and gashed his hand. The deep wound was cleaned and bandaged, but the injury hindered George Donner's ability to work and it eventually became seriously infected.

For the first eleven days of November the weather was cloudy and cool, with high temperatures near 40 degrees and rain and snow showers almost every day. Although there was initially little accumulation in the lower elevations east of Donner Pass, up on the summit above 7,000 feet, heavy snow was falling and piling up fast. Unknown to the pioneers, the icy barrier in the high country was becoming insurmountable.

The emigrants at Alder Creek were unable to build cabins due to a lack of manpower and deteriorating weather conditions. They were forced to pitch tents and hastily construct crude lean-tos using cut tree branches covered with canvas, blankets, pine boughs, and rubber raincoats. Jean Baptiste Trudeau, a 16-year-old from New Mexico who had been hired by the Donners back on the trail at Fort Bridger (Wyoming), later described their desperate situation: "Our little band worked bravely on until we came to Alder Creek Valley, where we had to stop, it being impossible to go further. The snow came on with blinding fury and being unable to build

Fallen tree at Alder Creek. Photo by Mark McLaughlin

cabins we put up brush sheds, covering them with limbs from the pine trees."

Their primitive accommodations were a rude shock for the prosperous Donner families. George and Jacob Donner were wealthy, gentlemen farmers with young children who, along with their neighbor James Reed and his family, had left their comfortable homes in Springfield, Illinois, on April 15, with bright hopes and dreams of a new life in California (Mexico). They outfitted nine wagons, three for each family, and hired a few teamsters and others to help them on the long journey. Like many of the other 1,500 emigrants traveling overland to California that year, they had heard of a salubrious climate that was "free of disease" and of land "free for the taking," even though it was owned and occupied by a foreign country. The idea of Manifest Destiny was sweeping the United States, part of a uniquely American philosophy which believed that not only is democracy rooted in land ownership, but as the influential columnist John L. O'Sullivan wrote, "It is our Manifest Destiny to overspread the whole of the continent which Providence has given us for the development of the great experiment entrusted to us."

Land, climate, and greater economic opportunity for his family were what inspired 60-year-old George Donner (some ages are disputed by historians) to uproot his family and head west with his wife Tamzene "Tamsen" (44), a teacher who planned to open a school in California. They brought their five young girls. The two oldest, 13-year-old Elitha and Leanna (11) were from George's second marriage, while the three youngest, Frances (6), Georgia (4), and Eliza (3) were from his third marriage to Tamsen.

George's younger brother Jacob "Jake" Donner decided to join the adventure too. Jacob in his mid-fifties and accompanied by his wife Elizabeth "Betsy" (45) and their five children: George (9), Mary (7), Isaac (5), Samuel (4) and Lewis (3). Traveling with them were two sons from Betsy's previous marriage, Solomon (14) and William (12) Hook. To help with tending the livestock, maintenance duties, and hard physical labor during the overland migration, the Donner families hired four men; John Denton, Noah James, Hiram Miller and Samuel Shoemaker.

For many years, historians believed that one of the Donner families pitched their lean-to against this tree. Recent archaeology disproved this. Photo by Mark McLaughlin

James Reed (45), an ambitious, Irish-born furniture maker, had also decided to bring his family west that year. That included his wife Margaret (32) and their four children, Virginia (13), Martha "Patty" (8), James Jr. (5), and little Tommy who was only three years old. Like the Donners, Reed was financially successful so he also hired people to help along the way. Their five employees consisted of a cook, Eliza Williams (31) and her brother Baylis (about 24), as well as three teamsters, Milford "Milt" Elliott, James Smith and Walter Herron. All the teamsters hired for the trek were in their mid-twenties.

Like other pioneers taking the California Trail in 1846, the Donner and Reed families followed the advice of emigrant guidebooks and purchased hundreds of pounds of flour, bacon, sugar, coffee and salt for the long trip. The food supplies, along with household goods, tools and other equipment were loaded into stout farm wagons. Livestock included horses, spare oxen and milk cows. The Reeds also brought along their five dogs, including Cash, the children's pet.

Despite her age (about 70) and an advanced case of tuberculosis, Margaret Reed's bedridden mother, Sarah Keyes, insisted on joining the caravan. Mrs. Keyes' youngest son had emigrated west the previous year and Sarah hoped that she would see him again before she died. To make the journey as comfortable as possible for his mother-in-law, James Reed had one of his wagons modified. A side entrance like a stagecoach was installed, complete with steps, and extensions were built over the wheels for additional storage and a sitting area. Spring seats and a few small beds for Grandma Keyes, Mrs. Reed, and the children would provide a relatively comfortable traveling experience. The wagon, later dubbed a "pioneer palace car" by Virginia Reed, was also equipped with a large mirror and a little wood-burning stove to warm them on chilly mornings. Despite the wagon's plush amenities, however, Sarah Keyes would die on May 29, about six weeks after they departed Illinois.

SUTTER'S FORT/SACRAMENTO VALLEY

Much had happened in the five months since Sarah Keyes was buried. The Donners and Reeds had joined a large wagon train, but later they and others split off and formed a new company. George Donner was elected the captain, creating the Donner party about July 19 or 20. Nearly 60 more emigrants joined the Donner-Reed families at various points along the trail as they all made their way west that year. Among them were six families: Breen, Eddy, Graves, Keseberg, McCutchen, and Murphy, which added many more children to the company. (The Donner-Reed families already had 16 young children among them.) At Fort Bridger, the Donner party consisted of 74 people and 19 wagons. James Reed had supported taking a shortcut through the Wasatch Mountains east of the Great Salt Lake, a fateful decision that added weeks to their travel time and used up precious supplies. The company lost livestock and wagons crossing the Utah desert, and then lost more cattle to Indian's arrows as they plodded along the Humboldt River across present-day northern Nevada.

Captain John A. Sutter. Courtesy California State Parks. Sutter's Fort Archives

James Reed found himself at Sutter's Fort in the southern Sacramento Valley, while his wife and children were snowbound at Donner Lake. Reed must have felt he was living a bad dream. In a tragic moment on October 5 along the Humboldt River, Reed had killed his friend John Snyder in what some people considered an act of self-defense after Snyder lashed out with his bullwhip handle and struck Reed in the head drawing blood. Hired as a teamster, Snyder was driving a wagon for the Graves family when his team of oxen had become tangled with those pulling one of Reed's wagons, handled by Milt Elliot. Reed responded to Snyder's angry outburst by pulling his knife and the two men had come to blows. In the heat of battle, Reed plunged his weapon into Snyder's chest, killing him. Banished from the wagon train after the mortal fight, Reed had to leave his wife and children behind. Accompanied by his employee Walter Herron, the two men raced ahead to reach Sutter's Fort to get help. They arrived in the Sacramento Valley at the end of October, just before a severe snowstorm blasted the mountains.

John Augustus Sutter played a major role in pre-gold rush emigration to California. Among his many contributions, he was particularly generous in providing assistance to relief efforts for the Donner party. Born of Swiss parents in 1803, John Sutter arrived in California in 1839. The following year he was granted Mexican citizenship and acquired an enormous land grant of 75 square miles at the junction of the Sacramento and American rivers. At that time Sutter was appointed the official representative of the Mexican government in the Sacramento River region.

Using Hawaiian and American Indian labor, he built a primitive outpost of grass huts. By 1844, Captain Sutter commanded a substantial military-style fort, protected by a dozen cannon of various caliber and adobe walls 18 feet high and nearly three feet thick. The fort itself was surrounded by a thousand acres planted with wheat and 20,000 head of cattle

Sutter's Fort. Courtesy California State Parks. Sutter's Fort Archives

grazed over the range. Calling his enterprise New Helvetia (New Switzerland), Sutter employed hundreds of people; local Indians were paid a token amount for their work, usually beads or credit to buy merchandise in his store. Sutter's Fort later became the foundation for modern Sacramento.

Despite Reed's exhaustion and the warning from Captain Sutter that it was too late to try and cross the snow-covered mountains, he was determined to bring food to his family, as well as to those who had banished him from the company. Reed was hopeful that Charlie Stanton had reached the emigrants with provisions, but with the unexpected snow he knew they would need extra help over the Sierra. Walter Herron, however, was weak from their grueling trek so he decided to remain at the fort. Thirty-year-old William McCutchen, who had accompanied Stanton in their own earlier effort to get help told Reed he was ready to risk his life again to save his wife Amanda (25) and infant daughter Harriet who he had left behind.

In early November, Reed, McCutchen and two Indian guides rode east from the fort with provisions generously supplied by Sutter. Shortly after they departed the fort it began to rain in the valley with more snow falling in the upper elevations. It rained off and on for several days as they ascended the Sierra west slope, but when they reached the head of Bear Valley at elevation 4,500 feet, heavier rain and sleet warned of worsening conditions in the higher terrain. They were able to secure the flour and horses, but were unable to kindle a fire. Reed wrote, "At the lower end of the [Bear] valley, where we entered, the snow was 18 inches in depth." After another mile or two it was 24 inches deep. The next day's march brought them to snow nearly four feet deep and the horses began to flounder, some of them almost smothered in snow. Here the Indians deserted Reed and McCutchen and returned to the fort. Without snowshoes the two men could make no headway. Frustrated and defeated, they gathered their horses together and backtracked out of the mountains to safety.

DONNER LAKE

The nine Breen family members were among the first of the company to arrive at Donner Lake at the end of October. There wasn't much snow on the ground near the lake yet, but the pass ahead was ominously white with deep drifts. The lead group of emigrants attempted to climb the pass, but deep snow thwarted their efforts. Returning to the east end of the lake the Breen's crowded into an existing cabin, built by the Stephen-Townsend-Murphy party in 1844. The other emigrants crawled into their wagons for the night.

Aligned along an east-west aspect, Donner Lake lies at 5,937 feet above sea level at the eastern base of Donner Pass and the Sierra crest. The east end of the lake averages more than 15 feet of snow a year, but spillover from the pass dumps even greater amounts on the west end of the lake. Donner

Donner Lake looking west toward pass. Photo by Mark McLaughlin

Lake occasionally freezes over during the winter months; in 1846 the frozen lake frustrated the emigrant's efforts at fishing. Sitting for hours in the cold waiting for a fish to bite was too much for the weak and starving pioneers.

Fourteen-year-old John Breen later described the weather conditions as his family led the struggling wagon train to Donner Lake: "In the morning it was very cold, with about an inch

A ring around the sun or moon often indicates an approaching storm. Photo by Mark McLaughlin

of snow on the ground…and, at last, the clouds cleared, leaving the towering peaks in full view, covered as far as the eye could reach with snow. It was sundown. The weather was clear in the early part of the night; but a large circle around the moon indicated, as we rightly supposed, an approaching storm."

Their fear of another storm was justified; in fact, it was already raining along the California coast. On October 31, the *U.S.S. Portsmouth* was still anchored in Monterey Bay. That afternoon, the sailor on duty reported: "Fresh breezes from the southwest and cloudy with rain." The barometer was falling and the air temperature a chilly 53 degrees. It wouldn't be long before the cold front would surge into the mountains bringing with it wind, cold and snow. Fair weather prevailed in the high country for much of the day, but later that evening increasing clouds led to snow again.

The coastal storm ripped into the mountains overnight, piling fresh powder onto the summit's existing drifts. The desperate pioneers at Donner Lake tried to make it over the 7,135-foot-high pass the next day, but as they ascended the rugged trail the snow grew deeper until it reached the axles of the wagons. At one point they realized they could go no farther. When they returned to Donner Lake, they "found it raining in torrents."

Edwin Bryant, who had traveled along with the Donners until Fort Bridger, later published a book about the journey. He was correct when he wrote, "The snow commenced falling on the Sierra, two or three weeks earlier in 1846 than is usual, and when this [Donner] party arrived at the foot of the pass they found it impossible to proceed from its depth."

Although any mountain man could have told them otherwise, the pioneers in the Donner party were completely ignorant of the mountain climate: John Breen wrote, "It cleared off in the night and this gave us hope; we were so little acquainted with the country as to believe that the rain in the valley was rain on the mountain also, and that it would beat down the snow so that we might possibly go over [the pass]. In this we were fatally mistaken." The next day a blizzard was raging over the rugged Sierra peaks.

John Breen was the oldest son of an Irish Catholic family recently arrived in the United States from Ireland. They were naturalized American citizens who had taken up farming in

The Breen family. Courtesy California State Parks. Sutter's Fort Archives

Keokuk, Iowa, before deciding to move again to the Pacific coast. His father, Patrick (51) and mother Margaret "Peggy" (about 40), were bringing their seven children to California for a better life and a place where Catholicism was the national religion. John's siblings included five brothers, Edward (13), Patrick Jr. (11), Simon (9), Peter (7), James (5) and a baby sister, Isabella, only six months old. The Breen's owned three wagons and were accompanied by their friend Patrick Dolan who had one wagon of his own. Dolan and the Breens had started traveling with the Donner party during the approach to Fort Bridger and the "Hastings Cutoff." At that point there were 74 people and 19 wagons in the Donner Company.

Many of the most critical problems experienced by the Donner party can be attributed to their decision to take the Hastings Cutoff. One of the most popular trail books at the time was Lansford Warren Hastings' *The Emigrant's Guide to Oregon and California*. Hastings, a lawyer from Ohio, had become a nationally known California land promoter after visiting the Pacific Coast in 1843. His guidebook provided extensive, yet dubious details about the climate and economic potential for agricultural development in the region. Regarding the mildness of California's climate, Hastings stated, "No fires are required, at any season of the year, in parlors, offices or shops, hence fuel is never required, except for culinary purposes."

Hastings discussed Oregon in his book, but his main sales pitch for emigrants was California's beneficial climate: "The best evidence that can be adduced, in reference to the superior health of this country, is the fact that disease of any kind has seldom been known." He implored his readers to "exchange the sterile hills for the deep, rich and productive soil, and uniform, mild and delightful climate, of this unparalleled region." Hastings' description of California as a paradise on earth inspired a contemporary to write: "[Hastings] is the Baron Munchau-

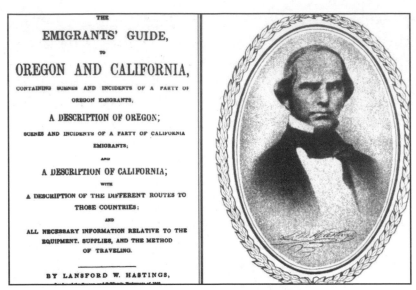

Lansford Warren Hastings. Courtesy Frank Titus Collection

sen of travelers in these countries." (*The Adventures of Baron Munchausen* is a book of tall tales, noted for the protagonist's exaggerated and fantastic accounts of his adventures.)

Despite Hastings' over-the-top hyperbole that painted the Sacramento Valley as the Eden of the West, for many emigrants the guidebook was considered the best source for trail information. In his book, Hastings mentions a new 300-mile shortcut that would save time and energy. The "Hastings Cutoff" detoured from the traditional California Trail by heading west from Fort Bridger through the Wasatch Mountains to the Great Salt Lake, and then 80 miles across the desolate Utah Desert towards the Humboldt River in present-day northern Nevada. Hastings' himself had only recently traveled part of his proposed route (by horseback — not with a wagon), but he didn't hesitate to send a message from Fort Bridger encouraging emigrant families to meet him there so he could personally guide them to California.

A few weeks earlier, the respected mountain man James Clyman had approached the Donner party regarding Hastings' shortcut, telling James Reed "…take the regular wagon track and never leave it — it is barely possible to get through if you follow it — and it may be impossible if you don't." Clyman and Reed know each other, having mustered together in the 1832 Black Hawk War, but Reed was obstinate in his confidence of Hastings. He replied, "There is a nigher route, and it is of no use to take a roundabout course."

Map showing California Trail and Hastings Cut-off south of the Great Salt Lake.

Despite Clyman's sage advice and Tamsen Donner's misgivings about Hastings' reliability, on July 19, 1846, James Reed and George Donner made the left turn towards Fort Bridger. Hastings, however, did not wait for the Donner Company to reach the fort before he departed with emigrants already there. The long delays and physical challenges the Donner party suffered through on the "shortcut" ultimately added weeks to their traveling time, depleted their provisions and livestock, and set the stage for the frustration and anxiety that led to the Reed–Snyder conflict and killing.

Napa Valley

Two extended storm periods, one at the beginning of the month, and one at the end, characterized the weather of November 1846. In the lower elevations, rain saturated the ground and caused minor flooding. In the mountains, an estimated six to eight feet of snow fell on Donner Pass during the first storm period, which effectively closed the pass for good. A colder snowstorm at the end of the month piled snow up to six feet deep at Donner Lake, an unusual occurrence for so early in the season.

November's first storm blew through Yerba Buena (San Francisco) within 24 hours, but cloudy skies and cool temperatures indicated more unsettled weather off the coast. A vigorous low pressure system had stalled in the eastern Pacific Ocean in a position to generate bands of rain that surged onshore in rapid-fire succession. On November 3, another cold front whipped through the region. In Napa Valley, Edwin Bryant noted; "It rained all day…the black masses of clouds which hung over the valley portended a storm so furious, that we thought it prudent to take shelter under a roof for the night…In comfortable quarters, we roasted and enjoyed our bear meat and venison, and left the wind, rain, lightning, and thunder to play their pranks as best suited them, which they did all night." The next day Bryant wrote, "After traveling some ten or twelve miles, we crossed another range of hills or mountains, and reached Sonoma after dark, our clothing thoroughly drenched with the rain, which, with intermissions, had fallen the whole day."

The blustery winds and persistent rain showers generated flooding in the region and threatened Bryant's safety as he traveled by boat from Sonoma to San Francisco and then on to Sutter's Fort: "It rained incessantly on the fifth. Procuring a boat lying at the embarcadero, I left for San Francisco, but owing to the storm and contrary winds, did not arrive there until the morning of the seventh, being two nights and a day in the creek, and churning on the bay. I sailed early on the morning of the eighth for New Helvetia [Sutter's Fort], in a boat belonging to the sloop-of-war *Portsmouth*. We encamped that night at the head of Suisun having sailed about 50 miles in a severe storm of wind and rain. The waves frequently dashed entirely over our little craft."

The rapidly rising Sacramento River made up-stream navigation to the fort virtually impossible except with the aid of the tide. Bryant endured two more rainy days before the storm broke: "On the morning of the twelfth the clouds cleared away, and the sun burst out warm and spring-like. After having been exposed to the rain for ten or twelve days, without having the clothing upon me once dry, the sight of the sun, and the influence of his beams, were cheering and most agreeable."

In Monterey Bay, the *Portsmouth* tugged hard on its anchor chain as "fresh winds from the southeast and heavy rains" buffeted the warship. For nearly two weeks, the daily entries in the ship's deck log noted cloudy skies, gusty winds from the southeast and occasionally heavy squalls of rain. It wasn't until

November 12 that the winds shifted to the northwest and the skies cleared as high pressure took control. Once the stormy weather headed east, the crew on the *Portsmouth* prepared to sail for San Francisco. Before leaving the bay, however, Dr. Duvall noted, "Everything looks much greener than a week ago."

Indicative of how important the seasonal rains are to California, on November 7, 1846, the Monterey-based newspaper *The Californian* stated, "The rains have set in well this year."

DONNER LAKE

The extended period of rainfall that the editors in Monterey considered so beneficial for California was the just about the worst scenario that could have happened to the unfortunate emigrants caught in the mountains. At Donner Lake snow fell steadily, but with little accumulation at first. Up on the pass, however, periods of blinding snow pummeled the pioneers as they made repeated attempts to reach the summit.

Wind deposition builds snowpack along Sierra Nevada ridges. Photo by Mark McLaughlin

Years later, the recollections of the people who struggled through it were still vivid. John Breen wrote, "We soon found that the snow increased in depth as we advanced, and after traveling about two miles, it was so deep that the cattle could go no further and to make matters worse, another storm began."

The climate of the Sierra Nevada alternates between dry, mild summers and wet, cool winters with heavy snowfall. Donner Pass, at an elevation over 7,100 feet, is a storm-wracked region that averages about 35 feet of snow a year. The snowpack on the summit regularly reaches 10 to 15 feet deep, and on occasion exceeds 20 feet. Snowfall surpassing 10 feet in a single storm is not uncommon; the record single storm total on the pass is more than 15 feet in March 1982. Blustery winds can sculpt the snow into drifts of 30 feet or more. Despite their valiant attempts to cross the pass, the Donner party was up against some of the worst winter conditions in the country.

During one of their efforts to reach the pass, the emigrants grew so weary from battling the deep snow that they collapsed from exhaustion. Charlie Stanton and one of the Miwok Indian guides from Sutter's Fort pushed on to the summit where the snow was chest deep. Stanton reached the pass where he could see that traveling farther west would be nearly impossible, but he returned to the others to encourage them to push on. Someone had set a dead tree on fire and everyone was huddled around it for warmth. No one would budge. Once darkness settled over them, they lay down wrapped in their blankets for the night. In a few hours it began to snow again and by morning they were buried in it.

In an interview years later, Louis Keseberg recalled the event: "As it was, all lay down on the snow, and from exhaustion were soon asleep. In the night, I felt something impeding my breath. A heavy weight seemed to be resting upon me. Springing up to a sitting posture, I found myself covered with freshly-fallen snow. The camp, the cattle, my companions, had all disappeared. All I could see was snow everywhere. I shouted at the top of my voice. Suddenly, here and there, all about me, heads popped up through the snow. The scene was not unlike what one might imagine at the resurrection, when people rise up out of the earth."

Emigrants build log cabins for protection in November 1846. Courtesy Frank Titus Collection

Keseberg, a 32-year-old immigrant from Westphalia, Germany, was traveling with his wife Philippine (23), and two young children, Ada (3) and Louis, Jr. (1). Initially part of the Russell party, the Keseberg family began traveling with the Donner party when they took the Hastings Cutoff with the others. Louis Keseberg was well educated and spoke three languages, but he had little patience and some accused him of abusing his wife. A friend of his said, "Keseberg's greatest weakness was his unbridled temper, and one day he confessed that it was the source of considerable embarrassment to him. After his anger had subsided, he always realized his mistake and was extremely penitent. He gave every indication of being an honorable person."

After the emigrants awoke that morning and saw the new snow, they gave up and reluctantly trudged back down to Donner Lake. The Donner party split into small groups and spent the next week building shelters and preparing as best they could for an extended stay. The Breen family moved back into the deserted cabin. It was a small, rectangular structure, twelve by fourteen feet and seven to eight feet high. Built of pine saplings, and roofed with pine brush and rawhides, there was a single room and chimney at one end.

Louis Keseberg built a lean-to shed against the side of the Breen cabin for his family. William Eddy, a 28-year-old carriage maker from Illinois, borrowed some tools and with the help of William Foster and others, led the construction of another log cabin. Well-built and rectangular in shape, the

The Murphy family used this granite boulder as the west wall for their cabin. Photo by Mark McLaughlin

shelter was about 25 feet long, eight feet high, and 18 feet wide. The cabin incorporated a large granite boulder for its west wall. To maintain stability and sustain a snow load, the cabin partially enclosed the rock and used it for support. Known as the Murphy cabin, Eddy, his wife Eleanor (25), and their two young children, James (3) and Margaret (1), shared the cabin with the Murphy family from Tennessee and Missouri.

The large Murphy family consisted of a widowed mother, Levinah (36), and her five children: John (15), Mary (14), Lemuel (12), William (11) and Simon (8). There were also two married daughters and their families: Sarah Ann (19) and her husband William Foster (30) and their child, George who was about two years old. The other daughter was recently widowed Harriet Pike (18) and her two children Naomi (3) and Catherine (1). Harriet's husband, William Pike, had been accidentally shot and killed in October near the Truckee Meadows when a loaded pistol he handed to his brother-in-law William Foster discharged, sending a bullet into Pike's back.

A third shelter was erected about one half mile east of the lake cabins to provide refuge for the Graves and Reed families. It was a double cabin, with two rooms separated by a center-dividing log wall. There was a fireplace at each end of the structure and each room had its own doorway. The roof was nine feet high and constructed of logs covered with tree branches and dirt. Years later, William Graves said that each of the rooms was "about 16 feet square." None of the Donner Lake cabins had windows.

The twelve-member Graves family, originally from Marshall County, Illinois, had joined the Donner party at Fort Bridger. Franklin Ward Graves (57) and his wife Elizabeth (45) had eight children: Mary Ann (19), William (17), Eleanor (14) Lovina (12), Nancy (9), Jonathan (7), Franklin Ward Jr. (5) and

Elizabeth (1). A married daughter, 21-year-old Sarah, and her husband Jay Fosdick (23), were traveling with them.

The husbands of Mrs. Reed and Mrs. McCutchen were away, down in the Sacramento Valley, so the two women and their children along with Reed's employees, Milt Elliot, Eliza, and Baylis Williams, moved into the Graves' cabin. Charlie Stanton, a bachelor without a wagon and virtually no supplies, joined them. One of the unsung heroes of the Donner party story, Stanton had returned from the safety of Sutter's Fort at the end of October with provisions for the group.

Snow continued to fall and began piling up at the two camps. Dark clouds obscured the pass itself, but the emigrants realized that the drifts must be getting deeper by the day. Most of the families and all of the hired teamsters, including those at the Donner camp at Alder Creek, had few food supplies. The lucky pioneers with cows or oxen began butchering the meat to store it in the snow. The scrawny cattle and draft animals weren't needed anymore because there was no way to get a wagon over the pass, and without grass, the oxen wouldn't survive much longer on their diet of pine boughs. Fortunately the Breen family had managed to protect their livestock from the Indians better than anyone else and had enough to share with the Reed family.

Unwilling to give up and quit, William Eddy, a crack-shot hunter, borrowed William Foster's rifle and managed to kill a coyote and an owl, but the small bit of stringy meat didn't last long. He had hoped to bag a deer, but the deepening snow-pack had chased the herds to the lower elevations. A few days later, on November 14, in an amazing display of courage, Eddy tracked down a large, 800-pound grizzly bear. Using Foster's muzzle loading, single-shot rifle, he shot the bear once at 90 yards away. The wounded animal charged after Eddy, who hid behind a tree while trying to reload. He dodged the bear's desperate lunge and at point blank range shot it again and then clubbed it to death. He gave half the bear meat to Foster for the use of the gun, and then shared the remainder of it with the Graves and Reed families. (For those who doubt this story, in 1984–85, archaeologists excavated the Murphy cabin site and numerous fragments of grizzly bear bones were recovered. There is little doubt that Eddy shot and killed a bear, but Donner party archeologist Donald Hardesty points out that "species of North American bears are notoriously difficult to identify from fragmentary remains.")

William Eddy killing a bear near Donner Lake. Courtesy Emigrant Trails Museum

There were 81 emigrants trapped in the mountains at the two encampments, 59 at the lake and 22 at Alder Creek. Forty-four of them were hungry, frightened children.

When the weather finally cleared on November 12, fifteen of the strongest men and women at Donner Lake attempted to break out. They dressed warmly and took some dried beef as their only food. Charles Stanton, who had crossed Donner Pass twice and knew the route, volunteered to lead them west. The two Miwok Indian guides, Luis and Salvador, joined the desperate effort. The group was able to walk through the snow along the north shore of the lake, but once they ascended the steep slope up to the pass they encountered drifts up to 10 feet deep. They floundered helplessly in the fresh powder until they turned around in defeat, beaten by the mountain once again.

John Breen described their effort: "In a day or two the weather cleared, and some persons went to examine the road on the mountain to see if the cattle could cross. At night they returned and reported six feet of snow two miles from [lake] camp."

High pressure and fair weather dominated the region for the next eleven days or so. In the mountains, the days were mostly clear and pleasant with overnight temperatures below freezing. The snow settled and began to melt at Donner Lake and Alder Creek, but it remained deep in the higher elevations. Due to drifting and lack of sun exposure, the east face of the Sierra range will retain snow long after it has melted in other locations.

SUTTER'S FORT

After their failed rescue attempt, Reed and McCutcheon returned to Sutter's Fort. They now realized that Captain Sutter was right; there was no way for two men alone to reach the snowbound emigrants. Sutter wasn't worried yet. Based on information Reed had provided, he figured that the settlers had enough food to last several months at least. Neither man could know that Indians along the Humboldt River had decimated the livestock by killing or wounding them with arrows. Reed was concerned about his family, but there was little he could do at that point. He later wrote, "As soon as we arrived at Capt. Sutter's, I made a statement of all the circumstances attending our attempt to get into the mountains. He was no way surprised at our defeat. I also gave the Captain the number of head of cattle the company had when I left them. He made an estimate, and stated that if the emigrants would kill the cattle, and place the meat in the snow for preservation, there was no fear of starvation until relief could reach them. He further stated that there were no able bodied men in that vicinity [the fort], all having gone down the country with and after John Frémont, to fight the Mexicans. He advised me to proceed to Yerba Buena, now San Francisco, and make my case known to the naval officer in command."

Topographical Engineer John C. Frémont. Courtesy California State Parks. Sutter's Fort Archives

John Charles Frémont, an officer in the Army Corps of Topographical Engineers, was admired for his well-publicized explorations of the west. Known as the "Pathfinder," Frémont had made a mid-winter crossing of the Sierra Nevada just south of Lake Tahoe in February 1844. That year, James K. Polk was elected President of the United States on a platform that espoused "Manifest Destiny" and westward expansion to the Pacific Ocean. Due to a simmering dispute between the U.S. and Mexico over Texas, Polk ordered warships to the California coast for possible naval action and to hold off British, French and Russian ambitions to take over the country. For years, foreign powers had considered California "a plum ripe for the picking." In 1845, Frémont returned to northern California via Truckee Pass with a small expeditionary force under his command. A larger unit of troops entered southern California via the Owens Valley. In May 1846, President Polk declared war on Mexico.

On June 14, 1846, after being threatened with "extermination" by Mexican General Jose Castro, a small group of armed American settlers arrested General Mariano Vallejo in Sonoma. Considered an ally of the American effort to "liberate" California from Mexican rule, General Vallejo once said, "The Yankees are a wonderful people. If they emigrated to hell itself, they would somehow manage to change the climate."

Yerba Buena and San Francisco Bay in 1846. Courtesy Bancroft Library

Despite Vallejo's vocal support for an American takeover of California, the suspicious rebels sent him to Sutter's Fort for safeguarding. The pioneers then declared independence and proclaimed California a new Republic to be governed under laws heavily influenced by the U.S Declaration of Independence and Constitution. They hoisted a new flag that included a grizzly bear on it and the words California Republic. As soon as Frémont learned of this Bear Flag Revolt, he organized the rebels and his 62 troops into the California Battalion and led them against the Mexican army. In a series of small but violent engagements, Frémont's ragtag force secured much of the San Francisco Bay Area to be eventually handed over to the Americans.

DONNER LAKE

Given all the military and political activity going on in California, it's no wonder that people weren't thinking about the Donner party. Yet the emigrants holed up in the mountains were in a tough spot. Patrick Breen kept a diary in which he mentioned weather conditions, snowfall and accumulation. He also detailed daily life in the camps. On November 20, he wrote, "We now have killed most part of our cattle having to stay here until next spring and live on poor beef without bread or salt. It snowed during the space of eight days with little intermission, after our arrival here."

During the mid-November period of fair weather, high pressure deflected Pacific storms to the north. Sunny days and cold nights melted most of the snow around the lake cabins while the melt-freeze cycle formed a crust on the higher elevation snowpack. The clear skies and consolidated snowpack inspired another breakout effort. At dawn on November 21, twenty-two people, including nearly all the adult men, three women and three children from the lake encampment headed for the pass. The only person from the Donner camp at Alder Creek to make the attempt was John Baptiste Trudeau.

The group made good time traveling on the crusted snow and they succeeded in crossing the pass by sunset. Next morning, the emigrants got an early start, but trouble soon developed. Charlie Stanton had decided to bring Sutter's mules along in order to return them, but the animals were too heavy to walk on top of the firm surface of the snowpack. William Eddy urged Stanton to abandon the animals and offered to pay Sutter for them. Eddy tried to force the Indians Luis and Salvador to take the lead, but they were afraid of what Sutter might do if they returned without the valuable pack animals. Without Stanton or the Indians to guide them, the emigrants would not be able to find their way down the convoluted topography of the Sierra west slope. As if to reinforce the danger they faced, William Graves wrote, "We could see nothing but snow [ahead] and the tops of pine trees sticking out of it." There was no choice but to return to the lake.

SAN FRANCISCO BAY

Stuck in the mountains, the Donner party could only dream about the mild weather along the coast and in the valleys below them. For nearly two weeks during the middle of

November 29, 1846, deck log from U.S.S. Portsmouth. Courtesy John Cordine

November, the San Francisco area enjoyed mostly sunny skies and temperatures in the 50s along the water and warmer inland. Moderate to fresh winds from the northeast and northwest kept the damp fog bank offshore. During its journey from Monterey to San Francisco Bay, the *Portsmouth* struggled against gusty northeast winds, which delayed the ship's arrival at Sausalito. When the ship finally anchored, Dr. Marius Duvall wrote, "The appearance of the land around the Bay is much improved since June last when the *Portsmouth* came in. The recent rains have caused the grass to spring up, which gives everything the refreshing greenness of our spring at home. The weather is fine and warmer now than we found it in the summer."

A few days later, a strong low pressure system surged in out of the Pacific Ocean. Depending on location, this extended storm period lasted from November 25 to December 3. The *Portsmouth* began reporting "light squalls with passing clouds" on November 26. The next day the northwest winds had veered to the southeast, the barometer was falling fast and the sky overcast with rain. For a solid week, intense rain squalls and gale force winds lashed the coastal areas of northern California. It wasn't until late in the day on December 3 that the rain finally ended in the San Francisco Bay.

Donner Lake

After the near success of the November 21 escape attempt, plans were made to try again. Franklin Graves and Charles Stanton were the only men in the company who knew about snowshoes. After they saw the miles of snow everyone would have to travel over west of the pass, they started to make snowshoes for the next effort. By now the snow was gone at the east end of the lake and communication had been established with the emigrants at Alder Creek. George Donner's gashed hand

Snow covered pine trees near Donner Lake. Photo by Mark McLaughlin

was not healing and his brother Jake was ill. Neither of them would be able to make a trans-Sierra trek anytime soon.

The pioneers chose November 26 (Thanksgiving Day) for the escape on snowshoes, but the coastal storm was quickly pushing east towards the mountains. Breen wrote, "Cloudy and looks like the eve of a snowstorm. Our mountaineers intend trying to cross the Mountain tomorrow if fair. Froze hard last night." That night, the storm moved in — just in time to thwart the escape attempt. The next morning, Breen wrote in his diary, "Began to snow yesterday in the evening, now rains or sleet. The mountaineers don't start today. Wind about west, wet and muddy."

Two days later, colder air had reached the region and the snow was eight to ten inches deep at the lake. On November 29, (Breen's diary dates may be one day off) Breen measured three feet of snow outside his cabin and it was still snowing heavily. That day he killed the last of his oxen. At the end of

November, the snow had reached between four and five feet deep. Breen wrote, "[Snow] looks as likely to continue as when it commenced. No living thing without wings can get about."

Successively colder storm fronts battered northern California for a week. Each impulse dropped snow levels in the mountains to lower and lower elevations. By December 1, the snow at Donner Lake was nearly six feet deep. Dry wood was increasingly hard to scavenge and simply getting around was getting difficult. "No going from the house," Breen wrote. "Completely housed up [and] looks as likely for snow as when it commenced, our cattle are all killed [except] for three or four of them. The horses and Stanton's mules [are] gone and cattle supposed lost in the snow. No hopes of finding them alive." The remaining unprotected livestock had wandered off and were buried in snow. The emigrants desperately searched for them with long sticks of wood with a bent nail on the end to grab tufts of hair, but with no success. Ironically, the mules that Stanton refused to leave behind were also missing and possibly buried in the snow. However, it's likely that Indians on snowshoes stole the valuable pack animals while the emigrants were hunkered down in the cabins. Either way, the animals were gone and lost as a potential food source.

The snowbound Donner party had plenty of time to re-read Hastings' book. Maybe they found one obscure statement about California's climate that he got right: "It may be truly said of this country, that December is as pleasant as May. The remarks here made, in reference to the mildness and uniformity of the climate, are applicable only to the valleys and plains, for the mountains present one eternal winter."

December 1846: Snowshoe Escape

3

DONNER LAKE

For the emigrants trapped at the Donner Lake and Alder Creek encampments, the severe storm that had raged at the end of November roared into December. It would be the first of three major storm periods that month. On December 2, the flow of moisture diminished and the snowfall let up a bit. That night the skies were partly cloudy, which led Patrick Breen to assume that the storm was over. The following day the southwest wind felt mild and hope for a thaw swept through the camp. Breen wrote, "Wind S.W. [and] warm but not enough so to thaw snow lying deep all around. Expecting it to thaw a little today." Later that day he added to his journal entry; "The forgoing written in the morning it immediately turned in to snow & continued to snow all day & likely to do so all night."

Hope for a mid-winter thaw of the kind experienced by the pioneers in places such as Illinois, Iowa, or Tennessee indicated a lack of awareness about the mountain climate that they were caught in. A classic winter weather pattern in the Sierra Nevada is prolonged periods of mostly sunny skies interspersed with intense Pacific-bred storms. This pattern well describes the winter of 1847. Despite these extended periods of dry, often pleasant weather, once the moisture-rich Sierra snowpack is well established, it creates its own chilled microclimate that resists rapid melting. This is especially true during the winter months of December, January, and February, when the angle of the sun is very low.

Donner Summit elevation sign on old U.S. Highway 40. Courtesy Frank Titus Collection

The snow depth at the camps already exceeded six feet with a much deeper pack in the higher elevations near the pass, and there were still more than four more months of winter weather yet to endure. The challenging hardships that the emigrants were about to face that winter were just beginning. Already the deep snow made it very difficult to gather dead wood and the cooking fires burned low. Soon the pioneers would have to burn their wagons constructed of oak. Hunting for food was simply out of the question.

Beginning on December 4, a high pressure regime took over. The dry conditions would last for five days and come as a welcome relief to the storm-weary emigrants. As the dome of higher pressure nosed in, the wind shifted to the northeast and the weather turned colder. Breen noted, "No sign of thaw…freezing pretty hard… snow deep." (Note: Some diary entries are edited for clarity.)

With food supplies already low, the sudden loss of the remaining livestock under the deep snow was a disaster. The fear and likelihood of starvation before rescue suddenly seemed very real. Only a couple of the families had any substantial beef butchered and stockpiled while most of them had just scraps of meat to live on until help arrived. Due to the lack of food, proper shelter, and an extreme state of exhaustion, many of the men were starting to lose their battle for survival.

Out of the 81 people in the mountains, there were 25 men and 15 women; the rest were children. At Alder Creek, Jacob Donner was very weak and ill, as were teamsters Sam Shoemaker and James Smith. Two immigrants from Germany, Joseph Reinhardt and Augustus Spitzer, were also in failing health. Reinhardt was at the Alder Creek camp

The few animals still active during a Sierra winter are small and elusive. Photo by Mark McLaughlin

while Spitzer was in the Keseberg lean-to at the lake. The condition of Baylis Williams was also getting worse every day. George Donner's wound had become infected and he too was laid up. There were only a few adults left at Alder Creek who were strong enough to gather firewood in the deepening drifts.

San Francisco Bay

For the first three days of December, gale force wind gusts (about 40 m.p.h.) howled from the southeast, while heavy rain drenched the northern California coast. By December 4, the

storm had pushed east of the bay. With the rising barometer came fair weather with chilly temperatures in the upper 40s to low 50s. On December 5, Dr. Marius Duvall was ordered to board the recently arrived U.S. sloop-of-war *Warren* anchored at San Francisco. Like the *Portsmouth*, the *Warren* was part of the Pacific squadron sent by President Polk to fight in the Mexican-American War. The conflict, however, failed to dampen Dr. Duvall's enthusiasm for the soft

John B. Montgomery, captain of the U.S.S. Portsmouth said, "The winter of 1847 was one of the severest rainy seasons that had visited the coast for years." Courtesy California State Parks. Sutter's Fort Archives

California climate. On December 6, he wrote, "A beautiful day — nearly calm. The country on the sides of the Bay has a very agreeable appearance — the green fresh grass has softened in a measure the ruggedness of the hills."

Donner Lake

From December 4 to December 8, a high pressure shield deflected all Pacific storms to north of the region. Under bright sunshine, the deep snowpack took on a magical beauty. Although he was suffering terribly from painful kidney stones, on December 6 Patrick Breen wrote, "Fine clear day... beautiful sunshine and thawing a little. Looks delightful after the long snowstorm." The following day, a storm system clipped the region, but luckily brought no snow, only cloudy skies and southeast winds. The fair weather brought hope to the stronger Donner party members who had not given up on escaping the mountains. "Stanton & Graves manufacturing snow shoes for another mountain scrabble...no account of mules," wrote Breen. Oxbows were split to use as frames for the snowshoes. Then the oxbows were sawed lengthwise and strips of rawhide served as the webbing.

The few days of clear and cold weather failed to bring the hoped for thaw, but it settled the pack and sustained their optimism. The reprieve in the weather ended on December 9 when snow blew in at 11 a.m. By the next morning a foot of fresh powder had accumulated at the camps. Breen wrote, "Snowed fast last night with heavy squalls of winds. Continues still to snow...very difficult to get wood today. Now about 2 o'clock. Looks likely to continue snowing...don't know the depth of the snow...may be 7 feet."

The following day the snow let up and temperatures felt mild, but the storm wasn't over. Intermittent showers and flurries over the next 48 hours led to a heavy snowstorm on December 13. "Snows faster than any previous day...wind N.W. Stanton & Graves with several others [are] making preparations to cross the Mountain on snow shoes. Snow 8 feet deep on the level."

ALDER CREEK

At Alder Creek, the 22 people trapped there were miserable. The tents leaked and their clothes were often wet. They relied on the last of their beef and rabbits and mice for food.

One by one the emigrants succumbed to exhaustion and famine. Photo by Mark McLaughlin

Joseph Reinhardt, who was near death, confessed to George Donner that he had murdered another German immigrant, Mr. Wolfinger, for his money. The crime had occurred at the Humboldt Sink. When Reinhardt and Spitzer returned from supposedly "helping" Wolfinger cache his goods, they told the other Donner party members that Indians had killed him. Wolfinger's wife, Doris, had stayed with the wagon company and had encamped with the Donner families at Alder Creek. Years later, Leanna Donner, who was 12 years old in 1846, recalled, "[Reinhardt] was taken sick in our tent. When death was approaching and he knew there was no escape, then he made a confession in the presence of Mrs. Wolfinger that he shot her husband; what the object was I do not know."

By December 20, Jacob Donner, Joseph Reinhardt, James Smith and Sam Shoemaker had all died. Baylis Williams succumbed on December 15. The rapid loss of the able-bodied men would be a real blow to the survival of the company.

SAN FRANCISCO BAY

Light southeast breezes and an overcast sky in Sausalito on December 9 indicated an approaching storm. By the next morning, fog and rain showers accompanied the falling barometer. Over the next two days, the rain increased in intensity until it peaked on December 13 when the *Warren* reported fresh gales from the southeast, constant rain and hail, and a low atmospheric pressure of 29.54 inches. Dr. Duvall, who was now back on the *Portsmouth*, wrote, "The gale continues."

By December 15, Dr. Duvall noted, "Today the clouds passed away and the sun again made its appearance." That day another ship arrived at Sausalito from San Diego, bringing news from John Drake Sloat, the Commodore of the Pacific squadron. Commodore Sloat was preparing for an assault on the Pueblo de los Angeles (Los Angeles), but the military action was not all focused in southern California. Dr. Duvall reported that recent intelligence indicated a large Mexican force just north of the bay of San Francisco. In case of an enemy attack, on December 17 the *Portsmouth* was moved to bring her broadside cannons to bear on Sausalito.

DONNER LAKE

On December 16, the "snowshoe party" (also known as the Forlorn Hope) got an early start. Weather and snow conditions were perfect. Breen wrote, "Fair & pleasant...froze hard last night & the Company started on snow shoes to cross the mountains. Wind S.E. [and] looks pleasant." Seventeen people started out in the Forlorn Hope, each equipped with a blanket, about eight pounds of "poor beef" and some sugar and coffee. The group was also supplied with a rifle, a few pistols, a hatchet and tobacco. (Smoking tobacco helped alleviate stress and hunger pains.) Only 14 members had snowshoes; the others tramped along behind. Their immediate destination was

Johnson's Ranch, the closest settlement in the Sacramento Valley. They estimated it was about forty miles away; the ranch was actually almost twice that far.

The snowshoe party included Sarah Fosdick, Mary Graves, William Foster, Sarah Foster, Charles Stanton, William Graves, Sr., Jay Fosdick, William Murphy, Harriet Pike, Lemuel Murphy, Patrick Dolan, the Miwok Indians Luis, Salvador, Mrs. McCutchen, William Eddy, Antonio, and "Dutch Charlie" Burger. (Antonio was a 23-year-old from Mexico who joined the wagon train at Fort Laramie. Dutch Charlie was an immigrant from Germany and part of the original Springfield group.) Some of the snowshoers were going for help to save their families; others were leaving so there would be one less mouth to feed. When bachelor Patrick Dolan joined the snowshoers, he left his beef with the Breens, with instructions that some should go to the Reeds.

Almost two out of three children survived. Billy Murphy was one of them. Courtesy California State Parks. Sutter's Fort Archives

Two of those without snowshoes, Dutch Charlie and 10-year-old William Murphy, turned back the first day. Lemuel

Murphy, who was 12 and also without snowshoes, valiantly struggled on. Within a few days, the members of the Forlorn Hope were several miles west of the pass, at Summit Valley, where the snow was about 11 feet deep. Another strong winter storm moved into the mountains on December 18 with snow and a cold, furious wind.

A few days later, on December 21, the shortest day of the year and the first day of winter, Stanton was left behind to die alone in the snow. Exhausted and snowblind, he was too weak from malnutrition to keep up and there was nothing anyone could do to help him. In the end, Charles Stanton, the brave bachelor who had risked everything to get supplies from Sutter's Fort for the wagon company, cannot save his own life.

Charles Stanton. Emigrant Trails Museum

The snowshoers were in a desperate situation, surrounded by deep snow with frostbite setting in and their supply of dried beef nearly gone. Luis and Salvador, the two Indians from Sutter's Fort, did their best to lead the pioneers in the blinding snowstorm, but they were effectively lost. About this time William Eddy found a small portion of bear meat that his wife Eleanor had secretly hidden in his pack. Eddy previously had to share any game he shot as the price of borrowing a gun, but this unexpected bonus was his alone. The precious protein was accompanied by a note from his wife signed, "Your Own Dear Eleanor."

SAN FRANCISCO BAY

The main storm period persisted for eight days, the result of a series of frontal bands rotating around a large low pressure system anchored off the coast. In the mountains, snow and wind started to batter the emigrants during the evening of December 18. Around San Francisco Bay the weather remained pleasant through December 19, but later that day the observer on the *Warren* reported fresh winds from the northwest shifting to the southwest. The wind shift and falling barometer was a sure sign of changing weather conditions. By the morning of the 20th, it was cloudy and raining in the San Francisco Bay with light southwest winds. The precipitation didn't last long, however, and the clouds cleared out by evening. By December 21, while members of the snowshoe party were fighting for their lives in a high country blizzard, temperatures had warmed up to near 70 degrees near Sausalito with fair skies and a light wind from the west.

The intense rain bands had moved south, which hampered the movement of Colonel John Frémont's troops in the California Battalion. At this point, Frémont's battalion consisted of about 350 trained military soldiers and volunteers, supported by 130 Indians and servants. They were organized into eight companies of calvary and artillery and represented a formidable fighting force. They had marshaled some 1,900 horses and mules, although many of them were "miserable, sore-backed skeletons." Frémont's force was delayed for three days at San Luis Obisbo by torrential rain. Some of the troops found shelter in the mission buildings while others improvised some protection as best they could. The downpour washed out their tents and threatened to "float them off solid land and out to sea."

Another moisture band surged onshore on December 22 with the barometer falling throughout the day. The moderate rain became heavy by Christmas Day. On the *Portsmouth*, Dr. Duvall wrote, "A merry Christmas has been bandied about today, but mal apropos. Raining and blowing terribly from the southeast, a gloomy day to all on aboard. One year ago [1845], I, in the *U.S.S. Constitution* off this harbor was enjoying as fresh a gale."

SANTA YNEZ MOUNTAINS (SANTA BARBARA)

After the storm broke at San Luis Obisbo, Frémont ordered his men to resume their forced march south in order to capture and gain control of the mission at Santa Barbara. Ultimately, the California Battalion was headed for Los Angeles to battle Mexican troops and rebels who had raised an insurgency to fight the Americans. General Castro had fled south with between 600 to 800 men to establish a defensive position near the Pueblo do los Angeles. To evade spies and avoid military skirmishes that would slow him down, Frémont planned his grueling march chiefly through the rugged hills and mountains. He kept his troops off El Camino Real, the main road that connected the Spanish colonial era missions and presidios along the California coast. The men grumbled that they were strong enough to defeat any number of Californians, but Frémont kept to his strategy.

The same weather conditions that spoiled the Christmas holiday for the sailors on the *Portsmouth* extended south down the California coast. On December 24, the battalion had reached the top of the east-west trending Santa Ynez Mountains that towered high above Santa Barbara located a few miles south of the range. From his vantage point in the mountains,

Mission Santa Barbara and Santa Ynez Mountains. Photo by Mark McLaughlin

Frémont used his spyglass to survey the terrain below. He saw no Mexican troops, just a lush, green plain and herds of grazing cattle. About 1,200 people usually inhabited the mission, but because of the Mexican-American War it was almost deserted. The principal summits in the Santa Ynez range are from about 4,000 to 4,700 feet above sea level, but Frémont, an experienced topographer and wilderness pathfinder, had found San Marcos Pass at elevation 2,225 feet.

It was Christmas Eve, and most of the men were in good spirits as they bivouacked on the pass and prepared for the difficult descent to Santa Barbara scheduled for dawn the next day. As the evening wore on, however, deteriorating weather conditions dampened their Christmas spirit. One of Frémont's men wrote, "The day was well gone before we reached the summit of the mountain. A cold wind swept the heights, the sun went down in a bank of ominous clouds, but there was no help for it. We must pass the night on this rocky crest. The fierce blasts almost blew away our little fires of light manzanita brush..."

That night, an intense storm swept in from the Pacific Ocean. One vivid eyewitness account was published in the 1883 *History of San Luis County:* "At midnight [Dec.24-25] the heavens were overspread with clouds, and the wind, which had freshened to a gale, bore to our ears the hoarse, prolonged roar of ocean. Our sailor men lay awake and listened, and predicted the roughest and nastiest kind of weather. The hurricane raging above our heads began to form torrents and cascades along our track. The narrow mule-path we were following became the bed of a foaming mountain river, which loosened stones and bowlders [boulders] and uprooted young trees in its course. Men and animals were swept before it. Shoeless and coatless, and hugging their arms under their thin blankets, many of them [soldiers] sank down, benumbed and exhausted." One man said, "It was as if the ocean which lay at the foot of that mountain had been lifted up and poured bodily over them."

The road down from the rain-lashed mountain was an extremely steep gully worn by years of loggers hauling lumber. Sandstone ledges forced the men to lower their heavy guns by hand. During the course of the day, the rain changed to sleet. By nightfall, they were still negotiating the precipitous descent and were forced to suspend the operation until daylight. Some of the men tried to protect themselves from the severe storm by finding shelter in the rocks, while others proceeded down to the plain to build fires and stand knee-deep in mud. The next morning dawned bright and clear with all men accounted for, but 150 valuable horses had been killed in the tempest.

Donner Lake

Just before the first storm impulse blew into the Sierra on December 18, Patrick Breen was in a bright enough mood to comment upon the beauty of the winter landscape. He wrote, "Beautiful day...sky clear. It would be delightful were it not

Storm-swept Donner Pass. Photo by Mark McLaughlin

for the snow lying so deep. Thaws but little on the south side of shanty." Breen mentioned that he saw no one from the other cabins. That night it began snowing at 11 p.m. and wind and snow squalls continued through most of the following day. After a brief break in the weather on December 20, the storm track shifted and subtropical air flowed into the region. The warmer air mass bumped snow levels to above 6,500 feet (Donner Lake's elevation is 5,937 ft). Breen reported steady rain at the lake on Christmas Eve until midnight when colder air dropped the snow levels again. The snowfall rate peaked on Christmas Day when a blizzard dumped 20 to 24 inches. A few families celebrated the religious occasion, but for most of them, it was just another day of slow starvation.

The slow-moving storm finally cleared out of the mountains by December 26, but it left behind a snowpack about nine feet deep at the cabins on Donner Lake. The only firewood available to the emigrants were the dead pine trees scattered throughout the forest, but when they chopped one down it would plunge into the loose snow, become buried and the branches nearly impossible to remove. There was so little food left that the emigrants boiled strips of ox hides for any sustenance they could obtain from the disgusting gluey residue. "Dutch Charlie" Burger died on December 29 and was buried in the snow. At Alder Creek, the Donner families huddled in their blankets, virtually out of food and miserable in their leaky tents and lean-tos.

FORLORN HOPE — SNOWSHOE PARTY

No matter how bad conditions were at Alder Creek and the lake, the situation was much worse for members of the Forlorn Hope. The desperate snowshoers continued to push forward through blinding snowstorms and frigid conditions. They were without shelter and food, totally unprotected on the Sierra's

Patrick Breen. Courtesy California State Parks. Sutter's Fort Archives

upper west slope where winter storms are most intense. William Eddy saved the small bit of bear meat for himself so he could maintain his strength to gather wood and start fires. By December 27, four more snowshoers had died — Patrick Dolan, Antonio, Franklin Graves and young Lemuel Murphy. That night, after five days without food, most of the snowshoers resorted to cannibalizing the dead. Only Eddy, and the two Indians, Luis and Salvador, refused the meal.

During the last week of December, unsettled weather continued with occasional moisture bands rolling onto the coast and then into the mountains. Every other day rain showers pelted the sailors crewing the warships anchored in San Francisco Bay. After a foggy morning on December 30, the skies cleared and several men from the *Portsmouth* took the opportunity to do some military reconnaissance. Dr. Duvall wrote, "When we had reached the top of the hills, we all halted to gaze upon the interesting country around and below us — the Bay, the plain we had left and the mountain range covered with snow."

On New Year's Eve, Patrick Breen wrote, "Last of the year. May we with God's help spend the coming year better than the past, which we propose to do if Almighty God will deliver us from our present dreadful situation…Amen." He followed this prayer with his daily weather observations. "Now cloudy…wind east by south. For three days past, [it's been] freezing hard every night," he wrote. "Looks like another snow storm. Snow storms are dreadful to us."

4

January 1847:
Dire Straits

DONNER LAKE

New Year's Day dawned gloomy for the pioneers in the mountains, but fortunately for them, the big storm that Patrick Breen and the others had feared did not materialize. Light snowfall developed overnight on New Year's Eve as the wind direction shifted to the southeast, but the system was not strong enough to punch through the higher atmospheric pressure that was building over the region. The frontal passage generated only light precipitation, but the east wind that followed ushered in the coldest weather of the season.

Breen's diary entry on January 1 revealed the snowbound pioneers' increasing sense of desperation. They were in a dire situation — trapped in deep snow with virtually no food but ox-hides. "We pray the God of mercy to deliver us, from our present Calamity if it be his Holy will Amen. Commenced snowing last night… does not snow fast… wind southeast. Sun peeps out at times…provisions getting scant… dug up a hide from under the snow yesterday for Milt [Elliot]." Donner Lake was now frozen over and deep snow covered the ice. Fishing or hunting for food had become virtually impossible.

The month of January 1847 exhibited the classic Sierra weather pattern of periodic storminess separated by extended intervals of fair and dry conditions. There were two active storm periods, a three-day event mid-month and a more significant weather system during the third week. From January 2 to January 9, mostly clear skies reigned over the encampments. Under a protective dome of high pressure, the sun warmed daytime temperatures to above freezing, but with clear skies at night, any heat quickly escaped into the atmosphere after sunset.

The lack of wind, short daylight hours, low sun angle and extensive snowpack caused damp, cold air to pool in the Donner Lake and Alder Creek Valley basins. Occasionally, these conditions can form a chilling frozen fog the Indians called "pogonip." This atmospheric inversion (air at the surface is colder than air aloft) is a common feature in high mountain basins during periods of high pressure. During January, the average low temperature at these two sites is 14 degrees and the average maximum 40 degrees. On Donner Pass, the average January morning low is 12 degrees and the average afternoon high about 41. The slightly warmer maximum on Donner Pass, which is more than 1,000 feet higher in elevation, is the result of greater wind movement and lack of a persistent valley inversion.

Winter inversion near Alder Creek Valley. Photo by Mark McLaughlin

The weather may have been very cold and damp, especially in the morning, but starvation was the real enemy as it stalked them even as they huddled around their fires for warmth. In early January, Margaret Reed, nearly out of food and with four children to sustain, decided to risk everything and go for help. It had been nearly three weeks since the snowshoe party left and still no relief effort had arrived. Her oldest daughter, 13-year-old Virginia, went with her, as did Milt Elliot and Eliza Williams. Margaret Reed reluctantly left her three youngest children behind, as they were too small to bring along. They supplied themselves with a bit of dried beef, a compass and some matches.

On January 4, Breen wrote, "Fine morning…looks like spring thawing. Now about 12 o'clock…wind southeast. Mrs. Reed, Milt, Virginia and Eliza started about ½ hour ago with the prospect of crossing the mountain. May God of Mercy help them. Left their children here." (Five months later, in a letter Virginia Reed wrote to her cousin Mary Keyes, she explained how hard it was leaving Patty, James and Thomas with strangers: "[We] did not know whether we would see them again or not. We could not hardly get away from them but we told them [we would] bring them bread and then they were willing to stay. We went and was out five days in the mountains."

On January 5, Eliza Williams returned alone to the lake encampment, exhausted and suffering from frostbite. West of the pass, Margaret and Virginia continued to follow Milt Elliot who broke trail on crude snowshoes. They weren't sure how far they had to walk, but they thought that as long as the storms held off, they might have a chance to make it. Fortunately for them, high pressure dominated the region and an extended period of fair weather ensued. Temperatures were frigid at the lake, but the sunny skies gave encouragement to Patrick Breen that the winter may be ending: "Beautiful day…thawing some

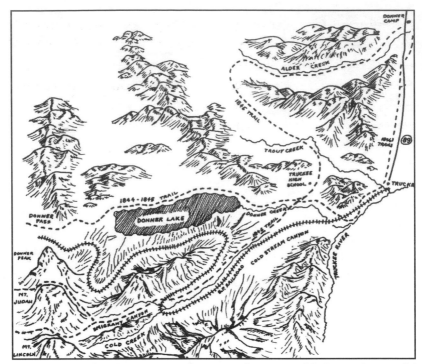

Detail map of Donner Pass region. — from Harold Curran's Fearful Crossing

in the sun…wind southeast. Snow not settling much. We are in hopes of the rainy time ending." By January 7, the dry weather pattern inspired a naïve optimism in Breen; "I don't think we will have much more snow." He erroneously believed that the winter storms were over, but he also noted that the snow had not melted much or diminished in depth.

High pressure kept Pacific storms at bay, but the Sierra snowpack was too deep and the distance to safety too far for the Reed women and Milt Elliot. Five days after they started, they returned hungry and exhausted to the lake. Virginia suffered from frostbite to her toes. After their arrival, Breen wrote, "Mrs. Reed & company came back this morning. Could not find their way on the other side of the Mountain. They have nothing but hides to live on." Margaret Reed had nothing to feed her children, so they split up. Patty Reed moved in with the Breen family, while Margaret took her other children back to the Graves' cabin. Virginia Reed later wrote, "We now had nothing to eat but raw hides and they were on the roof of the cabin to keep out the snow; when prepared for cooking and boiled they were simply a pot of glue." Everyone was demoralized. Breen wrote, "Prospects dull. May God relieve us all from this difficulty if it is his Holy will Amen."

FORLORN HOPE — SNOWSHOE PARTY

The extended period of cold, but fair weather during early January gave the ten surviving snowshoers (five men and five women) a chance to find their way down the tortuous Sierra west slope. They followed the North Fork of the American River, a rugged canyon more than 1,000 feet deep. At a point where the river ran south, they were forced to climb up from the canyon bottom over a ridge to the west. The terrain was so steep and rocky that the emigrants had to pull themselves up by shrubs growing in the crevices. From the top of the ridge, they descended toward the Bear River Valley, but not before getting their first glimpse of the green Sacramento Valley, still many miles away.

By New Year's Day, the snowshoe party had been struggling through the snow-covered mountains for 17 days. Their toes were black, their feet swollen and bleeding from repeated frostbite. Their boots and moccasins were falling apart so they tied fragments of blanket around them. Jay Fosdick, weak and snowblind, began to fall behind the others. In a few days they reached the snowline where they noticed oak trees interspersed with the pines and cedars. They were so hungry that they toasted the rotted leather thongs from their snowshoes over a fire to eat them. The members of the snowshoe party had hoped to reach the eastern rim of the Sacramento Valley

The Forlorn Hope struggled for weeks in deep snow. Photo by Mark McLaughlin

in about six days and had begun their escape from the lake with just enough food to make it that far. They had been walking for three weeks now, and they were still many miles from the closest settlement.

In their desperate fight for survival, they were forced to eat the flesh of their dead companions, as they died one by one. When all of the grisly fare was gone, William Foster, delirious and crazed with hunger, suggested killing the two Miwok Indians, Luis and Salvador. William Eddy was against the plan, and he told the Indians to flee while they could.

By January 5, there were only eight of the original 15 snow-shoers left — three men and five women. The higher proportion of women survivors in this group reflected the growing dominance of females among the surviving emigrants in the camps as the men died off. The first party to attempt the pass on foot had consisted of fifteen men and two women; the second try was comprised of sixteen men and six women. Finally, in the Forlorn Hope snowshoe party, the ratio was ten men and five women that were strong enough to try and escape. Some of the reasons for the women's greater survivability include more body fat, a lower metabolic rate and a temperament that is less prone to aggression. Nearly 15% of the males in the Donner party died as a result of violence, while there is no convincing evidence that any female member died violently. Women are also smaller and need less food to survive.

At this point the snowshoers were without food of any kind again, so William Eddy and Mary Graves took the flintlock gun and set out ahead of the others to see if they could hunt down a deer. They were out of the snowbelt and signs of game had become common. Sarah and Jay Fosdick, William and Sarah Foster, Amanda McCutchen, and the recently widowed Harriet Pike, were exhausted and remained behind. Two miles down the trail, Eddy observed crushed grass where a deer had recently rested. They

William Eddy — Survivor and rescuer. Courtesy California State Parks. Sutter's Fort Archives

crept along silently until at last they sighted an emaciated deer about 80 yards away, but Eddy was too weak to hold and sight the heavy weapon. Mary Graves cried, "O, I am afraid you will not kill it!" After two failed attempts to aim the rifle, Eddy was finally able to raise the gun vertically and as he slowly lowered the muzzle to track past the deer, he pulled the trigger and mortally wounded it. Eddy staggered after the animal until he was able to overtake it and kill it with his pocketknife. It was too far to carry any of the meat back to the others, so he and Mary Graves built a fire, roasted some of the venison and filled their bellies for the first time in weeks. That night, back on the trail, Jay Fosdick died of exhaustion. Now there were only seven of them left.

By the time William Eddy and Mary Graves returned the next day with the deer meat, the others were consuming Fosdick's corpse. They were all

delirious and every effort was being made to survive, no matter what it took. Both types of meat were dried over the fire and the group struggled on. About five days later, they came upon Luis and Salvador, lying helpless on the trail. The Indians had been without food for eight or nine days, and the last four days without a fire of any kind. Once again, William Foster suggested killing the Miwoks for food, and this time Eddy was unable, or unwilling, to stop him.

Harriet Pike whose husband was accidentally shot and killed, survived the Forlorn Hope. Courtesy California State Parks. Sutter's Fort Archives

(This is the only known instance of Donner party members killing human beings for food.)

Twenty miles after the murders of Luis and Salvador, the haggard survivors of the Forlorn Hope stumbled into a Miwok Indian encampment. Stirred to compassion by the pitiful appearance of the white people from the mountains, the Indians shared their acorn bread with them. On January

11, a strong storm system moved into Northern California and a cold steady rain began to fall. The seven survivors of the snowshoe party struggled through the rain from one Indian village to the next, where they were given a little bit of acorn bread and pine nuts to eat. A pair of strong Indian men took each victim by the arm and supported them as they all walked west. It was the Miwok tribe's kind generosity and steady nurturing that kept them alive for nearly a week during this last push to safety. Finally, late in the day of January 17, a couple of Indians carried William Eddy to a cabin in the American settlement of Johnson's Ranch, about 40 miles north of Sutter's Fort. The cabin's occupants were the Ritchie family who had arrived in 1846. Once the Ritchie's got over their shock at Eddy's emaciated condition, he was given food and water. Other members of the little community saddled horses and rode out to find the other survivors who had collapsed in the mud from exhaustion.

Wind-whipped snow on Sierra ridge. Photo by Mark McLaughlin

It had taken the Forlorn Hope thirty-three days to reach civilization and the hardships that they had endured would stun the California community. Once they blurted out that starvation and death threatened to wipe out the remaining Donner party members trapped in the mountains, the news spread like wildfire. It wouldn't be the first time that people had heard that there was trouble in the Sierra, but the news from the Forlorn Hope would prove shocking indeed.

The newspaper in Yerba Buena (San Francisco), the *California Star*, had already published an article under the headline: "EMIGRANTS IN THE MOUNTAINS. It is probably not generally known to the people, that there is now in the California mountains in a most distressing situation a party of emigrants from the United States, who were prevented from crossing the mountains by an early heavy fall of snow. The party consists of about sixty persons, men, women and children. They were almost entirely out of provisions when they reached the foot of the mountain and but for the timely succor afforded them by Capt. J.A. Sutter, one of the most humane and liberal men in California, they must have all perished in a few days. Captain Sutter, as soon as he ascertained their situation, sent five mules loaded with provisions to them [with Stanton]. A second party was dispatched with provisions for them [Reed and McCutchen], but they found the mountain impassable, in consequence of the snow. We hope that our citizens will do something for the relief of these unfortunate people."

SANTA CLARA VALLEY – MISSION SAN JOSE

For the past month, James Reed had not had much luck trying to organize a rescue effort. The countryside was in upheaval due to the war and there were few able bodied men and little in the way of available resources. On January 2, 1847, Reed, by then a captain in the California Battalion, fought in the "Battle of Santa Clara." It was a brief encounter that resulted after Frémont's troops had marched toward Los Angeles. About 100 Californians banded together to dramatize their resentment to the plundering of several local ranchos by some of Frémont's men as they traveled through the area. To protest these transgressions, the rebels kidnapped a half dozen Americans, including a U.S. navy lieutenant, who was out on a foraging expedition looking to acquire cattle, horses and saddles. The skirmish was quickly resolved, however, due to effective cannon shot by the Americans and the Californians' desire to settle their grievances without a major fight. The following day an armistice was arranged with U.S. assurance given that from then on, property would not be taken without proper formalities and compensation.

Fortunately for the starving emigrants in the mountains, the Mexican-American War was winding down in Northern California. In some ways, however, the war and its distractions proved beneficial for James Reed. In December, Reed had filed for land claims near the Mission San Jose for his family. In January, he was appointed the military officer in charge of the mission. Before he left the area to head back to the mountains, Reed spent time planting grape cuttings, barley, and pear and apple trees for the purpose of raising a vineyard and orchard. His efforts satisfied the homestead provisions for improving the land upon which a claim is filed, which gave Reed an early and important foothold in the region. With hostilities basically over in the north, the military could free up men and supplies and Reed could once again focus on rescuing his wife and children.

San Francisco Bay

During this extended fair weather period, clear skies, abundant sunshine and relatively little fog were the rule in the bay of San Francisco. Hostilities between the American and Mexican forces were ending and the United States military units in the northern portion of California could begin to relax and enjoy the cool but pleasant weather. It wouldn't be long before most of the navy's Pacific war fleet would be shipping out of San Francisco Bay for ports south and possibly more military action.

The high pressure regime eventually began to weaken, however, and by January 10, precipitation had moved into the Sierra. On January 11, the *Warren* log entry reported a rapidly

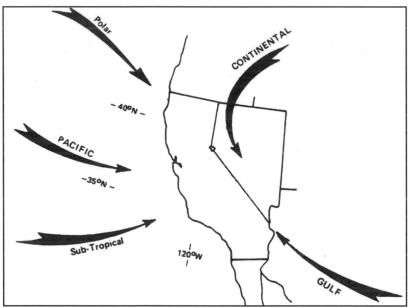

Prevailing wind vectors that influence California's climate. Drawing by Harold Klieforth

falling barometer, heavy rain and a gusty southeast wind. The storm was powerful, but a slow mover and intense rain showers lashed the coast for the next four days.

On board a warship bound from Valparaiso, Mexico, for Monterey, William T. Sherman (who later became a famous

Civil War general), noted the challenges of sailing the California coast. The English and Spanish charts that ship captains used differed by about fifteen miles in longitude, which could easily make the difference between a safe harbor and deadly offshore rock formations along the fog-shrouded Pacific coast. On Sherman's ship, an incorrect observation by the evening navigator placed the vessel about twenty miles south of their actual position. As they sailed north, searching for Monterey Bay, rain and low clouds obscured the coastline. On January 13, the cloud deck lifted slightly and they discovered that they had passed the northern headland of the bay.

In his memoirs, Sherman wrote, "The ship was put about, but little by little arose one of those southeast storms so common on the coast in winter, and we [were] buffeted about for several days, cursing that unfortunate observation on the north star, for on first sighting of the coast, had we turned for Monterey, instead of away to the north, we would have been snugly anchored before the storm. But the southeaster abated, and the usual northwest wind came out again, and we sailed steadily down into Monterey Bay." Sherman remarked how beautiful the place looked: "Every thing on shore looked bright and beautiful, the hills covered with grass and flowers, the live-oaks so serene and homelike, and the low adobe houses, with red-tiled roofs and whitened walls, contrasted well with the dark pine trees behind, making a decidedly good impression upon us who had come so far to spy out the land. Nothing could be more peaceful in its looks than Monterey in January, 1847."

DONNER LAKE

The emigrants snowbound in the high mountain camps hadn't seen green grass or flowers for months. Heavy snow developed on the evening of January 10 and over the next few days, about three feet of new accumulation was quickly added to the pack at Donner Lake. On January 13, Breen wrote, "Snowing fast. Wind N.W. Snow higher than the shanty. Must be 13 feet deep. Don't know how to get wood this morning. It is dreadful to look at." The next day, the snowfall diminished and the sun came out which lifted Breen's spirits: "Very pleasant today. Sun shining brilliantly…renovates our spirits. Praise be to God, Amen."

A weeklong period of fair weather followed the intense snowstorm. A dry cold front blasted through the region on January 16, which ushered in sunshine but much lower temperatures. In Sonoma, Dr. Duvall noted, "A cold night. Next morning [Jan. 19] was clear and delightful – the ground hard, and covered with a white frost reminding me of home. G.H. Gibbons, a medical doctor who lived in San Francisco, reported ice nearly ¼ inch thick in town. At the lake, Breen remarked that the snow froze hard the night before, but he was more focused on a possible rescue attempt that week. He had no reason to suspect help was on the way (the emigrants could only hope that the escape effort by the snowshoers had been successful), but he wrote, "Expecting some person across the Mountain this week."

Breen's optimism, however, was not supported by facts on the ground. The emigrants would have to wait for another month before help began to arrive. In the meantime, they would have to find a way to survive their ordeal. One by one they were slipping into delirium and closer to death. Mrs. Levinah Murphy was snowblind, while 17-year-old Landrum Murphy had gone "crazy" with hunger. They were all becoming restless and emotionally withdrawn, physiological symptoms of mental illness and delirium. On January 21, Milt Elliot arrived from the Alder Creek camp with news that "the Donners were all well," meaning that everyone there was still alive but in a similarly weak condition.

Donner Lake beginning to freeze. Photo by Mark McLaughlin

Eliza Williams, who couldn't digest boiled hides, had come to beg her employer Margaret Reed for meat. With her hungry children crying for food, Mrs. Reed could ill afford to share her last morsels of precious beef, and so Williams was sent away empty handed. Starving and desperate, some of the emigrants began to pull the ox-hides off their shelters. Patrick Breen wrote, "Provisions scarce. Hides are the only article we depend on...we have a little meat yet, may God send us help."

Shortly after dawn on January 22, the strongest storm of the season roared into the region. It reached blizzard proportions that night with heavy snow and gusty winds. The next day, Breen wrote, "Blew hard and snowed all night. The most severe storm we experienced this winter." The snow let up that afternoon and sunshine poked through the clouds, but the breakup was short-lived. Twenty-four hours later, another band moved into the mountains and snow showers increased again. On January 26, there was another break in the precipitation. In a clear display of his fluctuating emotions, Breen

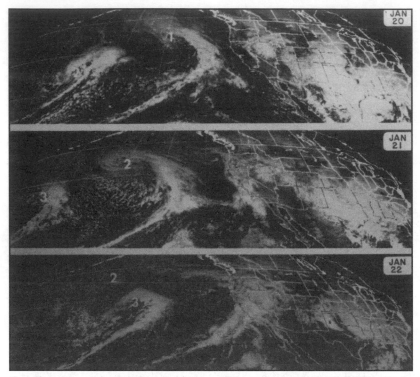

Satellite view of relentless and powerful storms pounding California in January 1983. Courtesy National Oceanic and Atmospheric Administration

again dared dream that winter was over: "Cleared up yesterday. Today fine & pleasant. Wind south. Hope [that] we are done with snowstorms." The next day, more snow and sleet swept down from the summit.

After the final frontal passage on January 27, a short period of higher pressure protected the region for the last days of the month. Spring-like weather and lively, chirping birds in the trees around the cabins indicated mild temperatures. The warm sun settled the snow a little which led Breen to speculate that if the snowpack melted off somewhat, maybe they could try to hunt some wild game. Any potential protein at this point would come too late for two children at the lake. During the storm, Louis Keseberg's infant son, one-year-old Louis, Jr., had died. A few days later, teenager Landrum Murphy was also gone. For many members of the Donner party, their own fate was just a matter of time.

Sutter's Fort/Sacramento Valley

Meanwhile, at Sutter's Fort, an effort was underway to organize and supply relief parties to rescue those trapped in the mountains. It wasn't going to be easy. There were probably less than twenty men in the southern Sacramento Valley and quite a few of them considered the attempt to reach the emigrants a suicide mission. The region was frontier country and the few ranches and settlements were widely scattered over what was now flooded terrain. The recent storm had engorged streams and rivers and travel was exceedingly difficult. To spread the alarm that the survivors of the Forlorn Hope brought to Johnson's Ranch, a letter dictated by William Eddy was dispatched by Indian courier to John Sinclair, an American with a ranch near Sutter's Fort.

The only government in the wake of the Mexican War was a confused and poorly organized mishmash of military and civilian laws and customs, some of which were based on the old Mexican system. Americans considered Sinclair a person of authority because he held the title of alcalde (mayor) of the Sacramento district. When Eddy's letter arrived at Sinclair's ranch with its message of famine, cannibalism and death, the alcalde immediately dispatched another courier to San Francisco with a letter containing the horrific news. Mrs. Sinclair gave the Indian courier from Johnson's Ranch a bundle of female underclothing to take back, for use by the women of the snowshoe party who had arrived at the ranch in a state of near nudity.

George W. Tucker, a 15-year-old at the time, later described how John Rhodes traveled from Johnson's Ranch to

Sutter's Fort today. Photo by Mark McLaughlin

Sutter's Fort during the flood. "Nothing could be done without help from other settlements," he wrote. "Sutter's Fort was the nearest point and it had been raining nearly all winter and the Country was all covered with water. Bear River was banks full so it could not be forded and if it could the Sacramento plains was one vast quagmire from there to Sutter's Fort, about 40 miles. Next morning John Rhodes crossed the river on our raft. He took his shoes in his hand, rolled his pants up above his knees and started for Sutter's Fort through water from one foot to four feet deep a good part of the way." During this storm, the Stanislaus River rose eight feet in one hour, overflowed its banks and covered the country for miles around.

Captain Edward M. Kern, the military officer currently in charge of Sutter's Fort (Fort Sacramento), offered $3 a day for any man willing to help in the rescue effort. Three men stepped forward to volunteer, but others would be needed to carry food provisions and contribute logistical support. Some men were skeptical that the military would pay the volunteers while others demanded an exorbitant $5 per day. After Sinclair and Sutter promised to be personally responsible for any wages, four more recuers signed up. Sinclair and Sutter also both agreed to supply food and horses. John Sutter sent his launch, the *Sacramento*, downriver towards San Francisco with the crew ordered to alert residents and request additional recruits and financial aid.

By the end of January, the first rescue party was organized, equipped and ready to go. These seven men were heroes, ready to risk their lives to save strangers caught in the remote mountain snow. They will battle deep drifts and deadly blizzards to fulfill their promise to rescue others in dire need. Other brave men would follow. Help for the Donner party was finally on its way.

February 1847: Rescuers Arrive! 5

Yerba Buena (San Francisco)

The First Relief Party had deployed from Sutter's Fort at the end of January, but other efforts were also underway to raise more men, money and supplies. On February 1, the weather in much of California was spring like with a warm sun and mild temperatures. But to the emigrants in the mountains, it must have seemed like the "eternal winter" that Lansford Hastings described briefly in his book. To make matters worse, another powerful storm system was barreling down from the Gulf of Alaska.

William McCutchen had been at George Yount's ranch in Sonoma trying to rally citizens there to help support a relief effort. Once McCutchen alerted the residents of Sonoma and Napa, they generously contributed hundreds of dollars for supplies. Mariano Vallejo, the ex-Commandante General of California, donated horses and mules from his ranch. Now that the war was over in northern California, James Reed was headed to Yerba Buena to appeal to the community and interim government officials there for assistance. (Named for the wild mint that grew there, "Yerba Buena" would be officially changed to "San Francisco" in March 1847.)

Reed had previously petitioned Robert F. Stockton of the U.S. Navy for help. At the time, Stockton was the governor and commander-in-chief of the United States Territory of California. Reed's petition read: "We the undersigned citizens and residents of the Territory of California, beg leave respectfully to present to your Excellency the following memorial...

Whereas, the last detachment of emigrants from the United States to California have been unable, from unavoidable

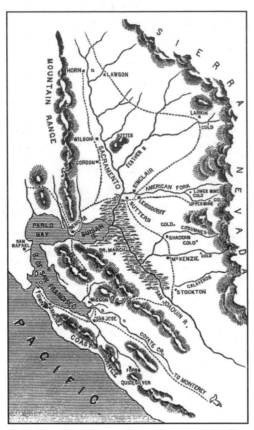

San Francisco Bay Area, Sacramento-San Joaquin Delta and Northern California river systems. Credit: 1847 map from "What I Saw in California" by Edwin Bryant

causes, to reach the frontier settlements, and are now in the California mountains, 75 or 100 miles east from the Sacramento Valley, surrounded by snow, most probably 20 feet deep, and being about 80 souls in number, a large proportion of whom are women and children, who must shortly be in a famishing condition from scarcity of provisions…"

Reed's pleas for help from the fledgling American government were published in the San Francisco newspaper *The California Star* on January 16, but little had been done. Now that the distraction of war was over, the citizens of San Francisco were ready and willing to help. On February 3, a public meeting was held to consider what should be done for the emigrants in the mountains. A steady rain soaked the city, but the gathering, held at a popular saloon, was well attended. Reed was too upset to address the crowd who had assembled to hear him speak, so Methodist minister James G.

Dunleavy stood up and gave an impassioned plea on his behalf. Dunleavy's words so stirred the residents of San Francisco that before the meeting adjourned, $700 was raised to purchase provisions, clothing, horses and mules.

It had been more than ten days since the snowshoe survivors had stumbled out of the snow country, but Reed and Mc-Cutchen were still unaware of how desperate the situation had become in the mountains. (There was no telegraph at the time and messengers had to struggle through flood conditions in the Sacramento Valley.) When Reed arrived at San Francisco, there was a letter waiting for him from McCutchen: "I am at Mr. Younts this morning with [trapper Caleb] Greenwood." The citizens are making a subscription to help us [save] our Families. We will start the first of February. If you come to Younts and we are gone you can overtake us at Sutters. We will go that way. You had better come in fast as there is no time to delay..."

The alarming news that the Forlorn Hope had brought out of the mountains reached San Francisco on February 5, when Sutter's launch *Sacramento* docked in the harbor. An open letter from Alcalde John Sinclair was read to the people of the city. Sinclair's letter graphically detailed the tragedy that was occurring in the high country as related by William Eddy and urged immediate action. A significant amount of money had been raised a couple days before for Reed's rescue group, but Sinclair's description of the suffering in the mountains incited an even greater outpouring of assistance for Donner party relief. Ominously, the cold rain and gale force winds that lashed San Francisco that day indicated more heavy snow in the mountains. Time was getting short to save the starving men, women and children trapped there. On the morning of February 5, Sinclair left for Johnson's Ranch to help launch the first relief effort.

Shortly after Reed's arrival in San Francisco, Caleb Greenwood showed up there, dressed in his worn and weathered buckskin suit. Greenwood, an 83-year-old mountain man, trapper and guide who was familiar with the inhospitable winter climate and rugged terrain of the Sierra, had traveled from Sonoma to give Reed first-hand advice on how best to reach the pioneers. Greenwood, who was not optimistic about the outcome, suggested that the rescuers might reach the high camps if they drove their horses in front of them to break the trail and then used them for food as they weakened along the way.

As the money and provisions poured in, two men offered their launch, the *Dice Mi Nana*, to transport James Reed and others to Fort Sonoma. Officer Selim Woodworth, U.S.N., volunteered to ferry supplies on a schooner from San Francisco to the delta and then north up the Sacramento River to the mouth of the Feather River. Commodore Joseph B. Hull, the top ranking naval officer in San Francisco at the time, appointed James Reed assistant to Woodworth and authorized him to "raise as many men, with horses, as would be required" at government expense. The generous donations by San Francisco citizens and military personnel had brought in enough money to purchase all the supplies necessary for the outfit. Provisions included 15 barrels of flour, one barrel of pork, 400 pounds of sugar, 17 pounds of tobacco, six frying pans, 24 blankets, 48 pairs of woolen stockings, and plenty of pants, flannel shirts and children's shoes. Since the U.S. Navy was now involved, Hull ordered Reed to "keep careful account of the necessary expenses of your expedition and submit the same to Mr. Woodworth for his approval with the necessary vouchers."

Abandoned mountain cabin buried by Sierra snow. Photo by Mark McLaughlin

DONNER LAKE

Snow began falling on the morning of February 2 at the mountain camps and continued all day with occasional breaks. The next day was cloudy and not as cold, but it was just the calm before the real storm. On February 4, Patrick Breen .wrote, "Snowed hard all night & still continues with a strong southwest wind...looks as if it would snow all day. Snowed about 2 feet now." But that was just the beginning. More snow fell on the following day until the storm peaked on the 6th when Breen reported, "Snowed faster last night & today than it has done this winter & still continues without intermission." At the end of the blizzard, Breen noted, "Ceased to snow last [night] after one of the most Severe Storms we experienced this winter...the snow fell about four feet."

On February 7, Breen dug his way out of the log cabin and climbed up onto the roof to shovel the overwhelming snowpack that was threatening to bury his family. The day was mostly sunny and pleasant with a mild breeze from the southwest, but the snow was about thirteen feet deep. The storm was over, but death was stalking the emigrants more quickly now. Harriet McCutchen, an infant who was left behind when her mother Amanda joined the Forlorn Hope, died on February 2. The Eddy's baby, Margaret, died two days later, followed by her mother, Eleanor, on Feb. 7. After his mother Eleanor's

William Eddy's wife Eleanor died before he could return to save her. Courtesy California State Parks. Sutter's Fort Archives

death, 3-year-old James Eddy was tended to by Levinah Murphy.

On February 8, bedridden Augustus Spitzer passed on, as did Reed's teamster Milt Elliot the following day. Elliot had been more than a loyal employee of the Reed family. Virginia Reed later wrote, "Our faithful friend who seemed so much like a brother. My mother and I dragged him out of the cabin and covered him up with snow. Commencing at his feet, I patted the pure, white snow down softly until I reached his face. Poor Milt! It was hard to cover his face from sight forever, for with his death our best friend was gone." In his memoirs, John Breen wrote, "Death had become so common an event that it was looked upon as a matter of course, and we all expected to go soon." Of the 81 people who had reached the High Sierra on October 31, fifteen had died and seven had reached safety in California. The remaining survivors, mostly children, were barely hanging on.

San Luis Obispo

Edwin Bryant, who had marched south with Frémont, spent January in southern California. During the second half of the month, Bryant experienced beautiful weather. "During this time, with the exception of three days, the weather and temperature were pleasant." he wrote. "It rained one day, and during two days the winds blew strong and cold from the northwest. The nights are cool, but fires are not requisite to comfort. The snow-clad mountains, about twenty-five or thirty miles to the east of us, contrast singularly with the brilliant fresh verdure of the plain."

The early February storm that had slammed the mountain camps, however, also blasted its way into Lower California. On February 3, Bryant noted, "The rain fell heavily all morning..." Two days later, he wrote, "The rain had fallen steadily and heavily all night and ...was pouring down when we started. We passed through the mission Luis Obispo just before sunset, intending to halt at a rancho about three miles distant. But, the storm increasing in strength, it became suddenly so dark in the mountain-gorge, that we could not distinguish the trail, and after wandering about some time, vainly attempting to find the house, we were compelled to bivouac, wet to our skins, without fire or shelter, and the rain pouring down in torrents."

The winter storms that were causing so much misery for the stranded emigrants to the north were nourishing the southern California landscape. As he made his way back to San Francisco for his overland return to the United States in June, Edwin Bryant couldn't help but notice the seasonal transformation: "The fresh vegetation has so much changed the face of the country on this river since we passed along here in December, that I scarcely recognize it. The grass is six or eight inches high in the bottom, the blades standing so thick as to present a matted appearance, and the hills are brilliant with flowers – pink, purple, blue and yellow." Bryant was very impressed. He stated without reservation; "For salubrity I do not think there is any climate in the world superior to that of the coast of California."

DONNER LAKE

High pressure during the second week of February began to settle the snowpack at the mountain camps. In areas exposed to sun, there was the feeling of thaw in the air. The period of sunny days and warmer temperatures were enough to inspire

Donner Lake snowdrifts. Photo by Mark McLaughlin

Patrick Breen to write, "We hope with the assistance of Almighty God to be able to live to see the bare surface of the earth once more." A weak cold front clipped the region on February 13, which brought a short period of rain to the coast and some snow to the mountains. A warmer weather system on the evening of February 15 raised snow levels, which brought rain to Donner Lake and Alder Creek. The following day, the frontal passage ushered in much colder air and for the next forty-eight hours instability in the atmosphere generated showers of hail [graupel]. Breen noted, "We all feel weakly today. Snow not getting much less in quantity."

For weeks now the snowbound emigrants had been wondering why no rescuers had arrived. They didn't know it, but help was just over the pass and coming quick. Not only did the First Relief bring some food and the first hope for survival the pioneers had had in months, but fair weather for the rest of February would give the rescuers and the survivors a chance to escape their snowbound prison under clear skies. The extended break in the storm pattern could not have been better timed.

Johnson's Ranch — First Relief

William Johnson's ranch, the most eastern American settlement in the Sacramento Valley, was the staging point for all of the rescue operations. The First Relief Party had left Sutter's Fort on January 31 and reached the ranch by February 2. They spent the next two days making packsaddles, drying beef and completing other preparations for their risky venture. The men intended to leave the ranch on February 4, but dark, ominous clouds indicated an approaching rainstorm, which kept them from heading into the mountains. They understood that time was of the essence, but it was late in the day and they were concerned about protecting their vital supplies. Reasin P. Tucker was co-captain with Aquilla Glover of the First Relief. Tucker noted: "There was every appearance of a storm coming…the party considered it best to remain [at Johnson's] until morning rather than risk the destruction of their provisions by the rain which in a short time fell in torrents accompanied by one of the heaviest hurricanes ever experienced on the Sacramento."

The men in the first rescue effort were quite aware that they were risking their lives by attempting to cross the California Mountains during winter, but they were also concerned about the human cost if they didn't try. Rescuer Daniel Rhoads later wrote, "Finally we concluded we would go or die trying, for not to make any attempt to save them would be a disgrace to us and to California far as long as time lasted. We started with a small company of men. We each carried 50 pounds of provisions, a heavy blanket and tools." William Eddy, who was still at Johnson's Ranch, joined the First Relief, but he had not regained enough strength to travel far. He had to be

helped onto his horse and was forced to turn back after a few days, but in March he would participate in the third rescue effort. (A Fourth Relief was organized in April primarily as a salvage operation.) Tragically, after risking his own life snowshoeing out of the mountains for help, Eddy was powerless to save his wife and young children.

As the First Relief marched toward the mountains, their horses and pack animals got mired down in muddy roads. At frequent in-

Rescuer Daniel Rhoads was 25 years old in 1847. Courtesy California State Parks. Sutter's Fort Archives

tervals they had to unpack their mules in order to pull them out of the muck. At one point, they had to swim their horses and pack animals across a flooded creek while the men carried the provisions over on a slippery log. It was tough going all right, but they knew conditions would get even worse in the higher elevations.

On February 6, torrential rain in the lower elevations soaked the men in the first rescue party. Member Col. Matthew Ritchie had started a journal: "Commenced raining before we got to camp. Continued to rain all of the day and night, very severe here. Laid by on the 8th [Feb.] to dry our provisions and clothing." After about five days, the men in the First Relief reached the snowbelt and soon they were struggling in snow three feet deep. After another few miles, they reached a place called Mule Springs where the snow was even deeper. At Mule Springs the party built a brush storehouse for the extra supplies and two men remained behind to guard it against hungry predators.

The snow depth was already overwhelming and yet they still had seventy miles to go, all of it up and over the storm-wracked spine of the Sierra. Some of the men were demoralized and several turned back. There were only ten of them left. The mules and horses had to be left behind once the snow became too deep so the men decided to make snowshoes. They were constructed by cutting pine boughs they stripped of bark and then heated over a fire in order to bend them in the shape of an ox-bow about two feet long and one foot wide. They used a latticework of rawhide for soles and attached them to their feet by means of rawhide straps.

On February 13, more rain and snow was falling as the First Relief reached the Bear Valley. (In November Reed and McCutchen had reached this location in their first attempt to reach the mountain camps. At that time, they found Mr. and Mrs. Curtis holed up in the snow with their wagon. After the Curtis' departed for the lower elevations, Reed and McCutchen cached their provisions in the wagon.) When the men in the First Relief dug down to the wagon to recover the provisions, they found the snow ten feet deep. Unfortunately, a bear or some other wild animal had destroyed the stashed supplies.

Due to the ever-increasing snowpack and darkening clouds that indicated another snowstorm, on February 15, several other men declined to go any farther. At this point, the First Relief was down to seven people. Captain Tucker, who had taken over the daily journal, wrote. "[With] only 7 men being left, the party was somewhat discouraged. We consulted together and under existing circumstances I took it upon myself to insure every man who persevered to the end five dollars per day from the time they entered the snow. We determined to go ahead and that night camped on the Juba [Yuba River] after traveling 15 miles."

The seven heroic men who kept trudging up the mountain were: Aquilla Glover, Reason P. Tucker, Sept Moutry, Ned Coffeemeyer, Joseph Sels, Daniel Rhoads and his brother John. Later, Sheriff George McKinstry of Sutter's Fort wrote, "Their names ought to be recorded in letters of gold." The next day, an intense snowstorm slowed their pace and they only made three miles. The snow was now nearly 15 feet deep. Each day the men built a fire on a platform of cut trees to keep the flames from melting into the snow. They also torched dead pines along the route as trail markers for them and others to follow. When the snow finally melted months later, the burned stumps indicated a snowdepth of almost eighteen feet.

As the men in the First Relief climbed the Sierra west slope, they gradually lightened their packs by leaving caches to be picked up on the way back. Finally, they reached the headwaters of the Yuba River and camped just west of Donner Pass where they "supposed the snow to be 30 foot deep." Aquilla Glover and Daniel Rhoads suffered from altitude sickness and their companions had to relieve them of their backpacks.

On February 18, they crossed the pass and descended down to Donner Lake where they reached the cabins at sundown. Instead of a lake, there was "a broad, clean sheet of snow."

The rescuers estimated that the snowdepth in the area ranged between twelve to eighteen feet. Deep enough on the east end of the lake that "the tops of the cabins were far below the surface." In a letter he wrote years later, Daniel Rhoads recounted their first encounter with the snowbound party: "We crossed Truckee Lake [Donner] on the ice and came to the spot where we had been told we should find the emigrants. We looked all around but no living thing except ourselves was in sight and we thought that all must have perished. We raised a loud halloo and then we saw a woman emerge from a hole in the snow. As we approached her, several others made their appearance in like manner coming out of the snow. They were gaunt with famine and I never can forget the horrible, ghastly sight they presented. The first woman spoke in a hollow voice very much agitated & said 'are your men from California or do you come from heaven.'... We gave them food very sparingly and retired for the night having some one on guard until morning to keep close watch on our provisions to prevent the starving emigrants from eating them which they would have done until they died of repletion." The rescuers tried to protect the famished emigrants from overeating, but

Trees in winter storm at Donner Lake. Photo by Mark McLaughlin

when 12-year-old William Hook got to Bear Valley and safety, he ate so much food that it killed him. (Hook was Elizabeth Donner's son from a previous marriage).

In the First Relief diary, Tucker wrote, "[We] found the people in great distress such as I never before witnessed, there having been twelve deaths and more ex-

pected every hour. The sight of us appeared to put life into their emaciated frames." On February 20, Tucker and two other men reached the Donner Camp at Alder Creek: "[We] found them in a starv-ing condition. Most of the men had died and one of them [Jake Donner] leaving a wife and 8 children. The two families had but one beef head amongst them. There were two cows buried in the snow, but it was doubtful if they would be able to find them. We left them telling them that they would soon have assistance. On the road back, I gave out, but struggled on until sundown when I reached the other cabins."

All of Peggy Breen's family survived. Courtesy California State Parks. Sutter's Fort Archives

Tucker and his men managed to escort six people out of the Alder Creek camp: the 19-year-old widow Doris Wolfin-ger and 16-year-old teamster Noah James, as well as the two oldest children from each Donner family. The dozen others there were too weak to escape. Despite entreaties from the rescuers, Tamsen Donner would not leave her ailing husband George or their three youngest children. Tucker insisted that teenager John Baptiste Trudeau stay at the Donner Camp; at this point he was the only one strong enough to chop wood to keep the fires going. Captain Tucker assured those left behind that more help was on the way and gave them a small amount of flour and dried beef.

The First Relief reached Donner Lake on February 18, 1847. Courtesy Frank Titus Collection

SECOND RELIEF — JOHNSON'S RANCH

Meanwhile, on Sunday, February 7, James Reed and Caleb Greenwood had boarded the launch *Dice Mi Nana* at San Francisco with other men who would help in the Second Relief operation. Instead of heading southeast towards Sutter's Fort, however, the Reed-Greenwood party traveled to Johnson's Ranch by a more direct route through the Sonoma and Napa valleys. Along the way William "Big Bill" McCutchen and other recruits joined them. Reed kept a journal and his quick pace from San Francisco to Johnson's Ranch revealed a burning desire to rescue his wife and children, whom he had not seen for four months. They reached Fort Sonoma on February 9 where they were given ten government horses and four saddles and bridles. The next day they left for Napa with five men. On the eleventh, they visited George Yount's ranch where they bought a pair of horses and hired three more men. Over the next week, Reed and his men traveled more than 100 miles to reach Johnson's Ranch. Along the way he purchased more horses and pack animals, as well as two wagon covers to use as tents. At one river crossing, Reed wrote "The water [was] up to the backs of our horses."

On February 17, they reached Hardy's Ranch at the mouth of the Feather River. Reed expected to rendezvous with Officer Woodworth and his launch loaded with clothes and provisions from San Francisco, but Woodworth was delayed by strong headwinds. The Second Relief also needed a ride across the muddy, rain-swollen Sacramento River to reach the east side. Fortunately, 25-year-old sailor Perry McCoon offered to both join the rescue effort as well as transport them across the river in his own boat. Reed and McCutchen crossed first, but increasingly gusty winds developed and the other men were temporarily stranded on the west bank. Reed and McCutchen continued on, however, and reached Johnson's Ranch the next day. Once there, they supervised the process of drying beef and making flour to take into the mountains.

After a brief delay, the other men of the Second Relief rejoined Reed at the ranch and they all began preparing their equipment for their expedition into the snow country. On February 23, the Second Relief started for the mountains and reached the low elevation snowpack two days later. The men started into the snow country with eleven horses and mules, each lightly packed with about 80 pounds of supplies. It was hard labor for the animals and they only made about six miles the first day. They left early in the morning the next day, hoping that the frozen snowpack would support the animals' weight. After only 200 yards they realized that pack animals were useless in the deep snow, so the men were forced to shoulder the heavy packs themselves.

FIRST RELIEF — HIGH SIERRA

On February 22, the First Relief left Donner Lake with twenty-three survivors in tow, including fifteen children. Among those trying to escape were John Denton, an Englishman who had been ill for weeks; three of the Graves children; Eliza Williams; 3-year-old Naomi Pike; Philippine Keseberg and her three-year-old daughter Ada; two of the Breen boys; 15-year-old Mary Murphy and her 11-year-old brother William; as well as Margaret Reed and all four of her children; Virginia, Patty, James and Thomas. They had not traveled far when two of the Reed family children were returned to the lake encampment. Mrs. Reed and her oldest daughter Virginia were able to keep up, but 8-year-old Patty and 3-year-old Tommy were too weak to continue and were

Everyone in Margaret Reed's family survived. Courtesy California State Parks. Sutter's Fort Archives

carried back to the Breen family cabin. When Patty, who would turn nine in a few days, said goodbye to her mother, she said, "Ma, if I don't see you again, do the best that you can." Five-year-old Jimmy Reed struggled to keep up, but Mrs. Reed encouraged him by saying, "Every step takes you closer to your father."

On February 23, they reached the first cache of provisions that the First Relief had hung in a tree on their way over the mountains, but wild animals had gotten there first and half of the dried meat was gone. The next day, Denton collapsed and was left behind to die. Rhoads wrote, "On the third day an emigrant named John Denton, exhausted by starvation and totally snow-blind, gave out. He tried to keep up a hopeful and cheerful appearance, but we knew he could not live much longer. We made a platform of saplings, built a fire on it, cut some boughs for him to sit upon and left him. This was imperatively necessary."

Mrs. Keseberg, who was too exhausted to carry her daughter Ada any longer, offered $25 and a gold watch to anyone who would bring her helpless child to safety. Despite her desperate offer, the rescuers were already loaded down with supplies or other small children and none of the other famished emigrants were strong enough to carry the little girl. Two days later Ada was dead. After losing her second child to starvation, Philippine Keseberg was inconsolable.

SECOND RELIEF — HIGH SIERRA

On February 26, Reed and his men had reached the lower end of Bear Valley and the primitive base camp of the First Relief. The men there were waiting for the first batch of Donner party refugees to be led out of the mountains. Some of the food supplies carried in by the Second Relief were left at the base camp to feed the famished emigrants who would

Overhanging cornices create dangerous avalanche conditions in the Sierra high country. Photo by Mark McLaughlin

arrive soon. More food and supplies were expected as soon as Woodworth and Greenwood arrived with men, provisions and clothes. Reed pushed on and camped that night at the upper end of the valley, where the men used the overnight hours to bake bread and sweet cakes.

Next morning, the second rescue expedition left camp early and traveled on a fine hard snow. Reed's diary entry tells the story of what happened when he met with the vanguard of pioneers being led to safety by the First Relief: "[We] proceeded about 4 miles when we met the poor unfortunate Starved people. As I met them scattered along the snow trail, I distributed sweetbread that I had. I gave it in small quantities. Here I met Mrs. Reed and two of my children — two still in the mountains. Bread Bread Bread Bread was the begging of every child and grown person. I gave to all what I dared and left for the scene of desolation." Tucker wrote that the meeting of Reed and his wife and two children was "very affecting."

That night, Reed wrote, "Now I am camped within 25 miles [of Donner Lake], which I hope to make [by] tomorrow. We had to camp soon on account of the softness of the snow." As the men in the First Relief led the survivors west out of the mountains, the Second Relief, which was headed east, camped on the Yuba River in five feet of snow. At the end of the February, they reached the summit region where Reed reported the snow 30 feet deep.

March 1847:
Great Escape

6

DONNER LAKE & ALDER CREEK

The seven brave men in the First Relief had pulled off a very risky rescue effort with little information about the route, a small number of personnel involved and minimal logistical support. In terms of organization, manpower, supplies and sheer physical ability, the Reed-led Second Relief was much better equipped. The men in the first expedition had to blaze their own route, which they marked by torching dead pine trees as they walked. For the second effort, there was strong logistical support provided by the U.S. Navy, which helped to quickly move a large amount of food, clothes, blankets and supplies into the remote Bear Valley staging area.

In the Second Relief, James Reed, Bill McCutchen, and Hiram Miller were each highly motivated to reach family and friends still trapped in the mountains. Reed's determination and fortitude was beyond question. McCutchen knew that his wife had survived with the Forlorn Hope and his only daughter had died at Donner Lake, but he was dedicated to saving as many others as he could. Miller was a friend of Reeds from Springfield who had been hired as a teamster by the Donners for the journey to California. About seven or eight other men, most of them trappers, hunters and mountain men handpicked by Caleb Greenwood, accompanied the trio. Old Greenwood himself did not make the climb into the mountains — he sent John Turner instead. Turner, a large and powerfully built mountain man, had been with the legendary explorer Jedediah Smith on their historically famous 1826 overland trek to

California. Greenwood's son Brittain, a well-known, 19-year-old trail guide in his own right, was one of the ten men of the Second Relief who traveled to the mountain camps.

Although storytellers tend to focus on the rescuers who "bravely hiked into the mountains to save fellow human beings," Donner Party Historian Kristin Johnson makes an important point: " We must not forget, however, that their heroism would have been in vain without the assistance of many others who contributed money, food, clothing, horses, and other supplies, or who transported provisions, maintained supply camps, brought the emigrants from the midway camps to the settlements, and opened their homes to the survivors."

Martha "Patty" Reed. Courtesy California State Parks. Sutter's Fort Archives

After their encounter with the first wave of refugees being brought out of the mountains, the men in the Second Relief pushed hard over the snow and were able to reach Donner Lake on March 1. On that day, Patrick Breen made his last diary entry: "Today fine & pleasant. Froze hard last night...10 men arrived this morning from Bear Valley with provisions. We are to start in two or three days & cache our goods here.

There is amongst them some old [mountaineers]. They say the snow will be here until June."

Once he arrived at the lake encampment, James Reed was overjoyed to find his children, Patty and Tommy, still alive. In his travel notes that were published later that year in the *Illinois Journal*, Reed wrote that he saw the top of a cabin just peering above the silvery surface of the snow. As he approached it, Reed discovered his daughter sitting upon the corner of the Breen cabin roof with her feet resting on the snow. Although the snow had settled about five feet since the last storm two weeks before, it was still as high as the Breen cabin, which was about eight tall.

The men in the Second Relief found both the lake and Alder Creek camps filthy and ghoulish, littered with waste and mutilated corpses half buried in snow. The rescuers dispersed part of the food they had with them — much of it they had cached on the trail to sustain everyone on the way back. Mc-Cutchen and Reed bathed the children and cleaned up Louis

Deep snow buried the shelters at Alder Creek. Photo by Mark McLaughlin

Keseberg who looked wretched. When Reed and some of the other men visited Alder Creek they found the Donner families in miserable conditions. They were subsisting on tallow made from the jerked beef trimmings left by the First Relief and whatever rabbit or rodent they managed to catch.

The rescue team immediately began preparing everyone for the great escape. The three oldest of Jacob and Betsy Donner's five children still at Alder Creek, Solomon, Mary and Isaac, were chosen to go, as they were considered strong enough to follow the men out of the mountains. (Jacob Donner had been among the first of the emigrants to die at Alder Creek.) Betsy Donner, who Reed described as "in a very feeble condition" remained behind with her two youngest children. Tamsen Donner had the strength to make it to Bear Valley, but she refused to leave her dying husband George, who was weak and helpless. When Reed told her that he expected another relief effort to arrive in just a few days with more provisions, Tamsen decided it was best to keep her young girls, Frances, Georgia and Eliza, with her. (Reed was counting on naval officer Selim Woodworth to lead a Third Relief into the mountains. Woodworth had established a base camp near Bear Valley with food and supplies, but he did not proceed farther east than that.)

With more help seemingly around the corner, Jean Baptiste Trudeau agreed to stay and help keep the fires burning. Before they left, the men moved Betsy Donner's tent-shelter to a different location away from the animal and human remains that lay scattered around it. After Reed had offered as much assistance as possible, he and the men returned to the cabins at Donner Lake.

On March 3, Reed and the other men in the Second Relief departed the lake encampment two days before another major storm system moved into northern California. There

Winter storm clearing over Donner Peak. Photo by Mark McLaughlin

were seventeen people being led to safety in this escape effort; one man, two women and the rest children, with nearly all of them under the age of ten. They consisted of the Breen family; Mary and Isaac Donner and their half brother Solomon Hook; Elizabeth Graves and her children; as well as Patty and Tommy Reed. The emigrants were hurried along as fast as possible over the frozen lake and toward the pass, but due to their weak condition the party only made two or three miles the first day. That night they camped on the north side of Donner Lake on a small patch of bare ground near the shoreline. The emigrants were in good spirits and optimistic that their ordeal was nearly over. (That same day, the eighteen surviving refugees being rescued by the First Relief reached Sutter's Fort.")

SAN FRANCISCO & MONTEREY

For the first few days of March, the weather in northern California was beautiful. In Monterey, Dr. Marius Duvall wrote, "The fine weather continues — the softness and balminess of the air are remarkable." For more than two weeks, high pressure had held off all Pacific storms, but on March 2, the falling barometer and heavy seas reported by the *Warren* anchored in San Francisco Bay indicated that a severe storm was approaching the coast.

By March 6, a cold and powerful Gulf of Alaska storm system had roared into the region. Within the relatively safe confines of the bay, the *Warren* was somewhat protected from the full impact of the tempest, but "heavy rain with north squally winds" indicated a major weather event. Within seventy-two hours, high temperatures had plunged from near 70 degrees to the low 40s. Onboard the *Portsmouth*, Dr. Duvall noted, "Cold disagreeable weather — a heavy swell settling into the Bay."

The passage of the cold front opened the door to rare "winter-like" conditions along the northern California coast. In San Francisco, temperatures dipped into the 30s and towering cumulonimbus clouds pelted the region with hail. Farther south in Monterey Bay, the weather was just as inclement. In his journal, Dr. Duvall wrote, "The last few days the [weather] has been excessively cold, and is disposed to continue so — the hills near here are covered with snow, and last night, some fell in town." (See Chapter 10 for more on San Francisco snowstorms.) This unusually cold and severe storm would be the last for Dr. Marius Duvall during his California tour of duty. On March 14, the *USS Portsmouth* shipped out for San Diego and destinations south.

Donner Pass & Summit Valley

The hail and snow along the coast were indicators of the vigorous weather system's origin in the frigid Gulf of Alaska. With significant cold air support and plenty of moisture to work with, this dynamic storm slammed into the Sierra Nevada and generated severe blizzard conditions in the upper elevations. The storm overwhelmed James Reed and the battered people in the Second Relief. By March 5, the party had managed to reach Summit Valley, near Donner Pass, where they rested for the night. The First Relief had camped here and left firewood for those that would follow them.

Summit Valley is a large alpine meadow and mixed pine forest surrounded by mountains. Located close to 7,000 feet in elevation and just west of the Sierra Crest, it is situated in a heavy snow zone where abundant precipitation feeds the headwaters of the Yuba River. Summit Valley is a very dangerous place to be caught unprotected in a winter blizzard.

Summit Valley and Lake Van Norden. Photo by Mark McLaughlin

To keep the emigrants alive during the night, a large fire was built on top of a platform of cut green logs that helped to slow the blaze from melting down into the deep snowpack. (Reed estimated the snow "twenty feet at least in depth.") Pine boughs were stacked on the snowpack to insulate the emigrants and keep them from getting wet as they lay under blankets around the fire. They were nearly out of food, so three men had been sent ahead earlier to retrieve the closest cache of dried beef that the Second Relief had left on the way in. (To protect the food from foraging predators, the bags of meat were tied to the top of a pine sapling and all the branches cut off. The strategy was only partially successful.)

As they huddled around the fire in Summit Valley, it was obvious that a severe storm was imminent. Reed wrote, "Sky looks like snow and everything indicates a storm…god forbid… the clouds still thickening. Terror, terror, I feel a terrible foreboding, but dare not communicate my mind to any. Death to all if our provisions do not come in a day or two and the storm should fall on us. Very cold — a great lamentation about the cold." Margaret Breen later described their bleak situation for author Eliza Farnham: "On the afternoon a snow storm set in very violently, and increased to blinding thickness before the evening was far advanced. We encamped early and the men of the relief party gathered and set brush in the snow, and threw up a bank against it, to break the storm off the fire and those who surrounded it. The storm was very violent all night."

For two days and two nights the storm lashed the mountains. In spite of the harsh weather conditions, the rescuers continued to chop wood to feed the fire that kept them all alive. The fire provided some heat, but they had no food. Reed wrote, "Still in camp, the last of our provisions gone. Looking anxiously for our supplies, none." The three men sent forward to obtain the first food cache five miles ahead had found it ransacked it by animals. They proceeded west toward the next cache, which still had some meat left, but before they could return to Reed and the others they were caught in the raging blizzard. Near death from cold and famine, they placed a portion of the meat in a tree located where Reed could find it and then pushed on down the west slope. Back at Summit Valley, Reed and the emigrants expected Woodworth and a Third Relief party to arrive at any time, but the naval midshipman never ventured far from his base camp located just above the snow line at Bear Valley.

Reed's journal entries continued, "My dreaded Storm is now on us. Commenced snowing in the first part of the night and with the snow commenced a perfect hurricane with the parents praying and crying and lamentation on account of the cold and the dread of death from the howling storm, the men nearly all night making fires, some of the men began to pray. Several became [snow] blind [including Reed]. I could not see even the light of the fire when it was blazing before me. Young Breen fell off his feet into the pit the heat of the fire had made in the snow to a depth of fifteen feet. It has snowed already 12 inches, still the storm continues. The light of heaven is as it were shut from us, the snow blows so thick that we cannot see 20 feet looking against the wind. I dread the coming night. After some time, wood being secured we had a great difficulty

Deep snow blankets the Sierra. Photo by Mark McLaughlin

in fixing a foundation for our fire, the snow having melted to a great depth. Still storming and very cold. So much that the few men employed in cutting the dry trees down have to come and warm about every ten minutes."

"Night closing fast and with it the hurricane increased — not quite so much snow falling as night before." Reed wrote. As the cold front itself rolled through the Sierra, blustery winds blasted the Summit Valley region: "At day light I discovered the Storm to Slack by hushing as it were entirely for a few minutes and then it would burst forth with such fury that I felt often alarmed for the safety of the people on account of the tall timber that surrounded us." A few hours later, the storm cleared out and bitterly cold air poured into the region.

William McCutchen recounted his own experiences at what would be called Starved Camp: "The second night Mr. Reed became snow blind and chilled through; he had over-exerted himself in securing shelter for the party. The rest of the men were disheartened, and would not use any exertion; in fact they gave up all hope and in despair, some of them commenced praying. I damned them, telling them it was not time to pray but to get up, stir themselves and get wood, for it was a matter of life and death to us in a few minutes. The fire was nearly out; the snow falling off the trees had nearly extinguished it before discovered; it was only rekindled by the exertion of Mr. Miller and myself. After we got the fire started I was so chilled that in getting warm I burned the back out of my shirt, having four on me; only discovering the mishap by the scorching of my skin."

When the storm finally broke, James Reed, who had recovered enough of his vision to walk, told everyone it was time to go. They had had no food for two days and another day or two at Starved Camp would kill them all. Five-year-old Isaac Donner had died during the storm and the others were extremely weak from famine and cold. The Breen and Graves families claimed that they were too exhausted to make it down the mountain and refused to leave the fire. Reed couldn't persuade them to get up and walk so he and Hiram Miller gathered a three-day supply of firewood to hold them until more help arrived. Reed and Miller were able to help Patty along and carry little Tommy Reed. Solomon Hook was strong enough to make it on his own.

Mary Donner, who had burned her foot in the fire and couldn't walk, stayed with the two families who remained behind. They had a small stack of firewood to burn, but there was no food to eat. The only sustenance available to the thirteen people left at Starved Camp were some seeds, a bit of tea and coffee, and a lump of sugar that Mrs. Breen had saved in her pocket. They didn't know it at the time, but it would be another five days before any help reached Starved Camp. Upset at their decision to stay behind, Reed told Patrick Breen (in front of witnesses) that if his children died, "the blood will be on his head, not ours."

Exhausted and without food themselves, the remnants of the Second Relief and their three young survivors struggled on toward Bear Valley. It was bitterly cold, and difficult and painful for them to walk. Several of the men had suffered frostbite and would lose a few of their toes. Reed wrote that after a day stumbling through the snow, "…they had no idea of the effect of the cold upon them until a fire was started, when reaction taking place in their limbs, their agony so intense and severe that they forgot for a time the cravings of hunger." Eventually they ran into John Stark and the other men of the Third Relief. There were under the command of Officer Woodworth who had organized the effort and provided them with food and blankets, but Woodworth himself was not with them.

William Foster was too late to save his son. Courtesy California State Parks. Sutter's Fort Archives

William Eddy and William Foster, the only two men who had made it to safety with the Forlorn Hope, were a driving force in the Third Relief rescue effort. Each of them had a young son still trapped at Donner Lake. Eddy, who had already lost his wife and daughter, hoped to save his little three-year-old boy James. Besides his son, George, who was four, Foster hoped to find his mother-in-law Levinah Murphy, and his brother-in-law, Simon Murphy, still alive.

ALDER CREEK

One by one, death was stalking the remaining survivors at Alder Creek and Donner Lake. Little Lewis Donner had died and his mother Betsy was fading fast. George Donner was also close to death. Tamsen and her three young daughters were weak, but still in relatively good shape. Jean Baptiste Trudeau continued to cut firewood and attend to the Donner girls while Tamsen nursed her husband as best she could.

Two men from the Second Relief, Charles Cady and Nicholas Clark, were assigned to stay with the remaining nine survivors at Alder Creek to assist them until the next rescue party arrived. At Donner Lake, Second Relief member Charles Stone stayed behind to provide for the five emigrants left there. Sometime after Reed's departure, Stone hurried up to Alder Creek. When Stone arrived, Clark was out tracking a bear that he had shot and wounded. What the two discussed is not known, but a short time later they decided to desert their posts. Maybe they were concerned that with another blizzard hitting the mountains, there was no guarantee that the next relief party would arrive before their limited provisions ran out. Whatever their reasons, Cady and Stone decided to leave immediately for the lake (without notifying Clark). Their ultimate intention was to get themselves out of the snow country and apparently with some treasure if possible.

Tamsen Donner became very distressed when she learned that Cady was abandoning them. She feared that the next rescue party might be delayed by stormy weather and her children might not survive another week or two in the tent. Tamsen paid the two men to take her three daughters with them to Bear Valley and safety. Cady and Stone accepted about $500 in cash and valuables from her and promised to do as she wished,

Snow-covered Sierra crest as seen from Alder Creek. Photo by Mark McLaughlin

but once they reached Donner Lake, they handed the girls over to Mrs. Murphy and left without a word. At this point, 37-year-old Levinah Murphy was mentally and physically exhausted and barely able to take care of herself.

George Donner, Jr. was the only Donner male to survive. Courtesy California State Parks. Sutter's Fort Archives

Cady and Stone waited out the storm in the former Breen cabin and then took off when the snow stopped. On their way through Summit Valley, they passed the dying refugees at Starved Camp, but they had nothing to offer them so they kept going. Later, when they caught up with Reed and the Second Relief as they assisted the emigrants down the west slope, cold stares greeted them for their desertion. Reed and the others were unaware of the ill-gotten booty that Cady and Stone carried in their packs. (In an interesting twist to this episode of abandonment, Charles Stone would return to the mountain camps again with the Third Relief effort. The impetus for this behavior may have been the wage of "$3 per day and $50 to any man who brought out a child not his own" offered by Woodworth. Without this incentive, the only men willing to join the Third Relief were William Eddy, William Foster, and John Stark, who "offered to go out without any reward beyond that derived from the consciousness of doing a good act." Eddy and Foster also paid fifty dollars each to get two other men to join them.)

Nicholas Clark found Charles Cady gone when he returned to the tents with a 70-pound bear cub he had tracked to a cave and shot. With a wild blizzard raging, there was little he could do, so Clark went to work preparing the fresh meat. Unfortunately, the food would come too late to save Betsy Donner who would die in a matter of days. The severe storm buried the tent shelters with so much snow, that the only indication that anyone was living there were the columns of smoke that rose from the two white mounds.

Years later, Donner Party historian, Charles McGlashan, talked to Clark about the killer March storm: "When Nicholas Clark awoke on the third day, the tent was literally buried in freshly fallen snow. Mr. Clark said he cannot remember how long the storm lasted, but it seemed as if it must have been at least a week [less than three days]. The snow was so deep that it was impossible to procure wood, and during all those terrible days and nights there was no fire in either of the tents. Sometimes the wind would blow like a hurricane, and they could plainly hear the great pines crashing on the mountainside above them, as the wind uprooted them and hurled them to the ground. Sometimes the weather would seem to moderate, and the snow would melt and trickle in under the sides of the tent, wetting their clothes and bedding, and increasing the misery of their situation. With Clark's assistance, they finally laid the child [Lewis Donner] away in a grave cut out of the solid snow."

SUMMIT VALLEY — STARVED CAMP

Fortunately for the rescuers and refugees, high pressure ruled from March 8 to March 20. On March 12, the seven men in the Third Relief reached Starved Camp to find eleven survivors huddled around a fire at the bottom of a deep snow pit. Mrs. Graves and her five-year-old son Franklin had died the first night after James Reed had left. Their bodies, as well as that of Isaac Donner, had been cannibalized. William Eddy later described what they found: "At 4 o'clock, they [Third Relief] arrived at the camp of those whom Mr. Reed had been compelled to leave. The fire at the Starved Camp had melted the snow down to the ground, and the hole thus made was about twelve or fifteen feet in diameter, and twenty-four feet deep. As the snow had continued to melt, they made steps by which they ascended and descended. The picture of distress, which was here presented, was shocking indeed."

Despite the extreme hardship and horrible conditions in which they existed, Peggy and Patrick Breen had kept seven youngsters alive for five days, including two infants and other children who were not their own. Eddy and Foster spent little time at Starved Camp, focused as they were on saving their own children at the lake encampments. It was left to Third

Winter conditions in Bear Valley. Photo by Mark McLaughlin

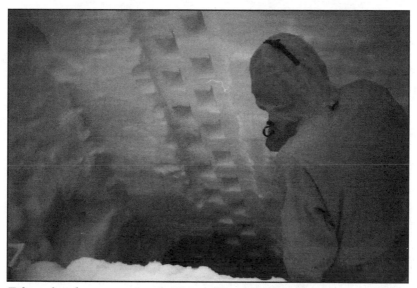

Fifteen-foot deep snow pit at the Central Sierra Snow Laboratory near Donner Pass. Photo by Randall Osterhuber

Relief members Charles Stone, Howard Oakley and John Stark to bring out the starving emigrants stranded there. They had not expected to find so many survivors at Starved Camp and the idea of taking eleven helpless people back to Bear Valley seemed ludicrous. Stone and Oakley proposed that they only bring out the injured Mary Donner and the three Graves children. They argued that the Breen family could wait for Foster and Eddy when they returned from Donner Lake. John Stark, however, was determined to leave no one behind and declared, "I will not abandon these people." When they left Starved Camp, Stone carried one-year-old Elizabeth Graves, which would earn him the $50 bonus for bringing out a child, while Oakley took out the injured Mary Donner. (Elizabeth Graves survived the journey to Sutter's Fort, but died there shortly after.)

Young James Breen never forgot John Stark or that he sin-gle-handedly saved the entire Breen family and the two Graves children. He later recalled: "To his great bodily strength, and unexcelled courage, myself and others owe their lives. There was probably no other man in California at that time, who had

the intelligence, determination, and what was absolutely necessary in that emergency, the immense physical power of John Stark. He weighed 240 pounds and was as strong as two ordinary men. On his broad shoulders he carried the provisions, most of the blankets, and most of the time some of the weaker children. In regard to this, he would laughingly say that he could carry them all if there was room on his back, because they were so light from starvation. I

Big John Stark single-handedly rescued nine emigrants. Courtesy California State Parks, Sutter's Fort Archives

distinctly remember that myself and Jonathan Graves were both carried by Stark, on his back the greater part of the journey. Mrs. Breen carried baby Isabella."

DONNER LAKE

On March 14, Eddy and Foster, and the two men they paid to accompany them, Hiram Miller and William Thompson, reached the cabins at Donner Lake. Like James Reed and the members of the Second Relief, the four men in the Third Relief recoiled in horror when they saw the mess of filth and mutilated bodies scattered around the cabins. For Eddy and

Foster, their hopes to save their sons were dashed when they learned that they had both died and their bodies cannibalized. The only people left alive at Donner Lake were Levinah Murphy, her 9-year-old son Simon, 32-year-old Louis Keseberg, and the three Donner girls, Francis, Georgia and Eliza. Tamsen Donner would soon arrive at the Murphy cabin to visit her daughters who had been left behind by Cady and Stone.

After the big March storm, Nicholas Clark had walked from Alder Creek to Donner Lake to check on the people that Charles Stone had abandoned. He was surprised to find Tamsen Donner's daughters there and had quickly returned to the tents to alert Mrs. Donner. The following day, Tamsen had hurried to the Murphy cabin to see her girls one more time and there she met the Third Relief party. With nobody left alive at Alder Creek except George Donner, and Betsy's 4-year-old son, Samuel, who were both slowly dying, Nicholas Clark and Jean Baptiste Trudeau decided to abandon the Alder Creek campsite. They met the Third Relief near Donner Lake and joined with them for the march to safety.

William Eddy tried to encourage Tamsen Donner to leave with them, but she could not abandon her husband George. She entrusted her three girls to Eddy and then returned alone to Alder Creek to stay with her husband until the end. The four men of the Third Relief each carried a child — the three Donner girls and Simon Murphy. Five survivors were left behind in the mountains. Louis Keseberg and Levinah Murphy at the lake, and three Donners at Alder Creek, George, Tamsen and their little nephew Sammy. Before the end of March, both George and Samuel would die and Tamsen would be on her own, alone at Alder Creek.

The fair weather ended on March 21 when the first of several storms rolled into northern California. Heavy snowfall in the Sierra and a softening snowpack discouraged the men in the Fourth Relief who were intent on reaching the last survivors still trapped in the mountain encampments. The men in this late March rescue effort included John Stark and William Foster, and others from the First and Second Relief

Margaret Isabella Breen survived Starved Camp as an infant. Courtesy California State Parks. Sutter's Fort Archives

parties. But Officer Woodworth said that instead of supporting another rescue operation, he and his men would focus on getting all the emigrants out of Bear Valley and down to Sutter's Fort where they could receive medical attention and proper nourishment. The snowpack east of the Sierra was melting fast, but in the high country the snow was still deep. Officer Woodworth reported, "When I left the mountains…the snow at the cabins was going off rapidly; but in Bear Valley and on the Yuba River, it was yet 20 feet deep on the level."

When the emaciated emigrants reached Johnson's Ranch, the pleasant weather and green countryside seemed like heaven on Earth. John Breen later recalled their arrival at the ranch: "It was long after dark when we got in the valley at Johnson's Ranch, so that the first time I saw it was early in the morning.

The weather was fine, the ground was covered with fine green grass, and there was a very fat beef hanging from the limb of an oak tree, the birds were singing from the tops of the trees above our camp and the journey was over. I [kept] looking on the scene and could scarcely believe that I was alive, the scene that I saw that morning seems to be photographed on my mind; most of the incidents are gone from memory through the lapse of years, but I can always see the camp near Johnson's Ranch."

Deep snow in 1983 buried this family's cabin on Donner Pass. Photo by Richard Steinheimer

Last Man Out 7

DONNER LAKE & ALDER CREEK

The Third Relief had left five people still alive at the two mountain camps. A fourth rescue party set out in late March to get these last survivors, but a barrage of storms and lack of logistical support by Officer Selim Woodworth discouraged the men from following through with their effort. No more rescuers from California would enter the snow country for another month. When a Fourth Relief finally climbed into the mountains in the middle of April, they found the snow three feet deep in Bear Valley and ten feet deep along the Yuba River.

William O. Fallon, a "very large, stout and rough" mountain man, was the leader of the seven men that comprised the Fourth Relief. These men had little hope of finding anyone but Tamsen Donner and Louis Keseberg alive. The effort was primarily a salvage operation, more focused on recovering material possessions for the survivors and themselves than a rescue effort for the last of the emigrants. They had made an agreement with Alcalde John Sinclair that they would recover as much property and money as they could from the Alder Creek camp, half of which would go to the estates of George and Jacob Donner, the other half going to the salvagers as payment for their services. Since they only expected to find one or two people alive, the men carried minimal food provisions.

The Fourth Relief reached Donner Lake on April 17, but Louis Keseberg was not there. Fallon and his men were appalled at the gruesome scene of dismembered and cannibalized bodies that surrounded the cabins. The camp was deathly quiet until they surprised three Indians hiding nearby who quickly fled leaving their bows and arrows behind. Finding no survivors, the men left for Alder Creek. About halfway there, they came upon a fresh set of footprints in the snow. The trail led directly to the Donner Camp where they found "property of every description, books, calicoes, tea, coffee, shoes, percussion caps, household and kitchen furniture, scattered in every direction, and mostly in the water." They found George Donner's body, but Tamsen was nowhere to be found. The men spent two days gathering up the most valuable property that they could carry in their packs, although much of it needed to be dried first. Aware that the Donner families had brought a considerable amount of money with them, they searched diligently for it, but found nothing.

Louis Keseberg. Courtesy Bancroft Library

On April 19, several of the men headed back toward Donner Lake. They tried to follow the mysterious track in the snow, but lost it due to the rapid melting of the spring snowpack. When they returned to the cabins at Donner Lake, they found Keseberg there. The men suspected that he was the one who had left the footprints in the snow and they asked him why he had hiked up to Alder Creek. They also questioned him about Tamsen Donner's whereabouts and the Donner money.

After weeks of isolation and the ordeal of spending the winter in the mountains, Keseberg was psychotic and delirious. Under interrogation, he admitted consuming Tamsen Donner's body, but that he had not killed her or stolen any of her family's money. Fallon and his men were suspicious, however, and searched him and the cabin. They found a bundle of silks and jewelry taken from the Donner Camp, two pistols owned by George Donner and $225 in gold. The men accused Keseberg of murdering Tamsen Donner and stealing the family's treasure. They threatened to hang him from the nearest tree unless he told them where the money was hidden. Under threat of death, Keseberg showed them were he had buried $273, an insignificant sum compared to the more than $10,000 in gold and silver George Donner had brought from Illinois. Keseberg told them that he had promised Tamsen Donner that he would carry the money to her children and insisted that the men in the Fourth Relief had no authority to take the money from him. (The Donner fortune was never found.)

Despite his pleas of innocence, for the rest of his life Louis Keseberg would be suspected of murdering Tamsen Donner, as well as others, including children. In 1879, Keseberg recounted Tamsen's last days: "At midnight, one cold, bitter night, Mrs. George Donner came to my door. It was about [four] weeks after Reed had gone, and my loneliness was beginning to be unendurable. I was most happy to hear the sound of a human voice. Her coming was like that of an angel from heaven. But she had not come to bear me company. Her husband had died in her arms. She had remained by his side until death came, and then laid him out and hurried away. He died at nightfall, and she had traveled over the snow alone to my cabin. She was going, alone, across the mountains. She was going to start without food or guide. She kept saying, 'My children! I must see my children!' She feared she would not survive, and told

Historic plaque at Alder Creek. Photo by Mark McLaughlin

me she had some money in her tent. It was too heavy for her to carry. She said, "Mr. Keseberg, I confide this to your care. She made me promise sacredly that I would get the money and take it to her children in case she perished and I survived. She declared she would start over the mountains in the morning. She said, 'I am bound to go to my children.' She seemed very cold, and her clothes were like ice. I think she had [fallen] in the creek in coming. She said she was very hungry, but refused the only food I could offer. She had never eaten the loathsome flesh. She finally lay down, and I spread a feather bed and some blankets over her. In the morning she was dead. I think the hunger, the mental suffering, and the icy chill of the preceding night caused her death."

On April 21, the Fourth Relief started for Bear Valley with packs that weighed 100 pounds each. Louis Keseberg followed them as best he could. On their return, they found the snow near the Yuba River from six to eight feet deep. Along the way, Keseberg noticed a bit of colored cloth sticking out of the melting snow. When he pulled at it, he discovered the body of his daughter Ada who had died while being rescued. Until that moment, Keseberg had assumed that his wife and daughter had survived the ordeal.

Alone and virtually helpless, Keseberg had been subsisting on human flesh at Donner Lake for weeks. Extracts from Fallon's journal were published on June 5, 1847, in the *California Star:* "Keseberg was found in a truly lamentable situation; a long subsistence upon the bodies of his deceased comrades had rendered him haggard and ferocious-looking...it is to be feared that his conduct in the mountains was far from justifiable, and a hidden transaction of guilt remains yet to be brought to light." The newspaper also published blood-curdling accounts of Keseberg's alleged activities based on Fallon's report.

Upon the Fourth Relief's arrival at Sutter's Fort, several of the men spread lurid tales about what they suspected had happened at Donner Lake. With no legal proof, they accused Louis Keseberg of theft, cold-blooded murder, rampant cannibalism and other atrocities. On May 5, at Captain Sutter's suggestion, Keseberg sued William Fallon and Ned Coffeemire for $1,000 for defamation of character in the court of John Sinclair, Justice of the Peace. The jury found in Keseberg's favor, but instead of $1,000 he was awarded only one dollar.

For the rest of his life, Louis Keseberg was vilified as a heinous criminal and called the "cannibal at Donner Lake." Eliza P. Donner Houghton, daughter of George and Tamsen Donner and only three years old in 1847, spent many of her adult years researching the history of this event. She eventually came to the conclusion that Keseberg had not murdered her mother. In April 1879, Eliza and Donner Party Historian Charles McGlashan interviewed Keseberg for the first time and encouraged him to make a statement in writing, which Keseberg was initially reluctant to do: "What is the use," he said, "of my making a statement? People are inclined to believe the most horrible reports concerning a man, and they will not credit what I say in my own defense. My conscience is clear. I am an old man, and am calmly awaiting my death. God is my judge, and it long ago ceased to trouble me that people shunned and slandered me."

The catastrophic 1862 flood wiped out Keseberg's Sacramento business. Courtesy California State Library

"I have been born under an evil star!" he finally wrote, "Fate, misfortune, bad luck, compelled me to remain at Donner Lake. If God would decree that I should again pass through such an ordeal, I could not do otherwise than I did. My conscience is free from reproach. Yet that camp has been the one burden of my life. Wherever I have gone, people have cried, 'Stone him! Stone him! Even the little children in the streets have mocked me and thrown stones at me as I passed. Only a man conscious of his innocence, and clear in the sight of God, would not have succumbed to the terrible things which have been said of me — would not have committed suicide! Mortification, disgrace, disaster, and unheard-of-misfortune have followed and overwhelmed me. I often think that the Almighty has singled me out, among all the men on the face of the earth, in order to see how much hardship, suffering and misery a human being can bear."

DONNER PASS

Spring came late to California in 1847 as high water in the Sacramento and San Joaquin valleys and deep snow in the Sierra continued to cause problems for travelers. When mountainman James Clyman crossed Donner Pass on May 1, he reported, "On the first day of May we succeeded in crossing the main summit of the California mountains, the snow being from 3 to 8 feet deep on the western slope, but on turning down the eastern side it was perhaps from 8 to 20 or even 30 feet deep, owing to the wind being always from the southwest when the snow is falling and carrying large quantities from the western side which is deposited on the east side."

Spring snowmelt at Yuba River headwaters. Photo by Mark McLaughlin

Trains traveling under Donner Peak are protected from avalanches by extensive snowsheds. Twenty years after heavy snow trapped the Donner Party, passengers could ride the first transcontinental railroad in comfort and safety any time of the year. Photo by Mark McLaughlin

John Craig was a member of a pack train heading east from Sonoma to Ogden, Utah, in the spring of 1847. Floodwaters in the Sacramento Valley delayed his planned April departure until after the middle of May. On June 7, Craig made his way over Donner Pass: "On my return home I supplied myself with seven mules with packs and all things necessary and in company with seven others we started for home on June 2. On the fifth day we crossed the peak of the California Mountains and had to travel about 35 miles over snow varying from 5 to 20 feet deep and rode over numerous mountain streams on arches of snow whilst we could hear the water roaring and dashing under our feet."

Better Days 8

There were 89 members in the Donner Company and 81 of them were trapped by snow in the mountains. It is a heart-rending story, yet it helps us to understand how people cope with severe hardship and seemingly insurmountable challenges. The lesson was not lost on California's civilian population or its interim government. When early winter storms battered the Sierra in October and November 1849, the first year of the gold rush, California's military governor, Major General Persifer F. Smith authorized $100,000 in emergency funding to finance relief teams for emigrants struggling along the Truckee and Carson trails, as well as the Lassen cutoff to the north.

Governor Smith was less concerned with starvation as most emigrants had sufficient provisions to reach California, but due to the huge numbers of people on the trail that year, some would inevitably need food and general assistance. The main focus was on the lack of forage for the oxen and cattle that pulled the wagons. If wagons had to be abandoned, it might backup the stream of emigrants trying to reach California before snow closed the passes. Teams of hired civilians and military personnel were sent eastward with water, food, and livestock to strategic locations in the mountains and desert to assist people trying to cross the Sierra into California. Similar operations were conducted in 1850 and 1852 when large numbers of gold-seekers and inexperienced overland emigrants were entering the new state. Never again would a wagon company be stranded in the high country without food or help.

After traveling overland to California in 1846, T.H. Jefferson published a detailed trail map of the route in 1849. Historian Dale Morgan considered it "one of the great American maps, an extraordinarily original production which will always have a special place in the cartography of the West." This *Map of the Emigrant Road from Independence, Mo., to St. Francisco, California*, was sold in New York City for the stiff price of $3 a copy. The map, with its printed *Accompaniment* of eleven pages, was published early enough in the year that at least one forty-niner, J. Goldsborough Bruff, carried a copy overland. Included in the *Accompaniment* text is the following advice, no doubt inspired by the Donner party tragedy. "The most difficult portion of the whole journey is the passage of the Californian Mountains, and particularly the descent of the western side. The only serious difficulty, however, is when you arrive late in the season, with a short supply of bread stuff, and encounter snow ten or fifteen feet deep. Those who expect to cross in safety must reach the Truckey [Donner] Pass by the 1st of October. The snow does not usually begin falling till November, and remains upon the ground more or less till May. If you arrive late, however, and encounter snow, do not attempt to cross the mountain, but scatter at once into small parties and retreat to the eastern base of the mountains, where you will find fertile valleys free from snow, which afford game, salmon, and roots, enough for small parties. You can winter there, and cross at the Truckey Pass when the snow is gone."

MORTALITY RATES

The mortality rates among the members of the Donner party represent the physiological and sociological differences between men and women, the strength of family groups and the age factor. In the Donner tragedy, females survived better than the males. Of the thirty-six who perished in the mountains, twenty-seven were men and nine were women. In the Forlorn Hope snowshoe party of fifteen people, eight men died; two men and all five women survived the long trek to safety. Females are longer-lived than males and suffer less mortality across all age classes. Women also have less muscle mass and a higher percentage of body fat (roughly 27% compared to about 15% in males). The fat is distributed in a larger proportion subcutaneously, which makes it an effective insulator. Two thirds of the men died, while two thirds of the women survived.

Donner Party victims are remembered in this historic plaque at Donner Memorial State Park. Photo by Mark McLaughlin

According to Donner party research conducted by archaeologist Donald Grayson of the University of Washington, women are twice as likely as men to survive extreme cold and hunger; more body fat, a lower metabolic rate and a temperament that is less prone to aggression make women the hardier sex when it comes to surviving this kind of disaster. Of the thirty males who died, 13.3% died as a result of violence, but there is no convincing evidence that any female member died violently. Family groups were important; all of the adult males who survived the entrapment (Breen, Eddy, Foster and Keseberg) were fathers. Every one of the single, bachelors over the age of twenty-one died. Of the children under the age of five, 62.5% died; no adults over the age of forty-nine survived, except for Patrick Breen who was fifty-one. The highest rate of survival was among children ages six through fourteen — of the twenty-one in that group, only two died.

One cause for the inordinate number of male deaths is likely the result of role expectations. Almost exclusively, the men were responsible for cutting trees and branches, gathering firewood, locating food, driving oxen and cattle, shoveling snow, repairing and sharpening large items and building shelters, along with other typically male duties. Once they were snowbound in the mountains, these predominantly outdoor activities exposed the men to wet weather and cold temperatures, which contributed to evaporative heat loss and sapped their energy. Ultimately, many of the adult men sacrificed their life to the group; only 27% of them survived, while 67% of the adult women and 87% of the adolescents lived.

From left to right: Nevada Governor Boyle, Martha "Patty" Reed, Eliza Donner Houghton, Frances Donner Wilder, and California Governor Stevens at the dedication of the pioneer monument at Donner Lake on June 6, 1918. Courtesy Frank Titus Collection

DONNER FAMILY

The two Donner families suffered greatly during the winter of 1847 — all four of the parents perished in the mountains as did several of their offspring. Their surviving children reached Sutter's Fort as orphans, but they all found good homes. At first, teamster Hiram Miller from Springfield acted as guardian for Frances, Georgia and Eliza Donner. James and Margaret Reed adopted George and Tamsen's daughter Frances, and later Jacob's daughter Mary. The citizens of San Francisco raised money to purchase town lots for George Donner, Jr. and his sister Mary. Fran-ces' sisters, Georgia and Eliza, were raised by a kind, elderly Swiss couple, Christian and Mary Brunner, who first lived near Sutter's Fort and then moved to Sonoma. The re-maining children were taken in by the fami-lies of their half sisters, Leanna and Elitha, who married young. All five of George Donner's girls married and had their own children, seventeen of them in fact. Nine were born to Jacob and Elizabeth's surviving children.

Tamsen's daughter, Frances Donner Wilder.
Photo author's collection

Most of the Donner family survivors enjoyed long and productive lives, except Mary who died while giving birth to her first child. Eliza Donner married Sherman Otis Houghton, a U.S. senator from California and the widower of her cousin Mary. Eliza belonged to several organizations, including the Red Cross, the Native Daughters of the Golden West and the Daughters of the American Revolution. In 1879, Eliza developed a friendship with Donner Party historian and author Charles McGlashan and in 1911 published *The Expedition of the Donner Party and Its Tragic Fate.*

MURPHY FAMILY

Teenager Mary Murphy had lost her mother and five other family members in the mountains, but within one month of reaching Johnson's Ranch she married William Johnson, co-owner of the ranch. Her husband was abusive, however, so she divorced him and married Charles Covillaud, who named the city of Marysville, California, for her. William Murphy became a lawyer and practiced in Virginia City, Nevada, until 1866 and later became city attorney of Marysville.

BREEN FAMILY

The Breen family, who survived intact, settled in San Juan Bautista. They were the first Americans to live there. Mr. Breen and other family members went on to become prominent figures in central California. The Breens operated an inn and Patrick became a rancher, school trustee, postmaster and Monterey County supervisor. The couple had one more child. When Patrick Breen died in 1868 at age 73, he left an estate worth $110,000. Their teenage son John struck it rich in the 1849 gold rush and brought home $12,000 worth of gold. The money enabled his father Patrick to purchase the house that Mexican General Jose Castro was letting them live in rent-free.

James became an attorney and served as a San Benito County district attorney and superior court judge. Edward became a prominent rancher and farmer who eventually owned large amounts of land in San Benito County and elsewhere. Their baby sister, Isabella, was a nursing baby during the ordeal at the mountain camps and the only infant out of six to survive. Thanks to her mother's care and nurturing, she miraculously lived and eventually gained fame as the last remaining survivor of the Donner party, dying at age ninety in 1935.

The Roman Catholic Breens moved to the Spanish mission in San Juan Bautista, California, built in 1812. Photo by Mark McLaughlin

EDDY FAMILY

William Eddy, who lost his wife, two children, and all of his material possessions, settled in Gilroy where he married and had three children. That marriage ended in divorce, but Eddy took another wife, a teacher who taught in Petaluma. He died there on Christmas Eve, 1859.

KESEBERG FAMILY

The sad legacy of the Keseberg family continued after Louis and his wife Philippine reached California. They had lost their first two children in the mountain snow, but the couple had eight more. Unfortunately, none of them lived past age thirty. In 1851, Keseberg purchased the Lady Adams Hotel in Sacramento, but it was destroyed by fire the following year. Between 1853 and 1861, he operated the Phoenix Brewery near Sutter's Fort, but that was destroyed in the January flood of 1862. After years of hardship, Louis and Philippine separated.

Keseberg died in 1895 at age 81, a friendless, penniless pauper. His wife and most of his children had preceded him in death. Mrs. Keseberg and two of their children were buried in the Sacramento City Cemetery. Louis Keseberg's buried remains near the Sacramento City Hospital were later disinterred in a mass grave removal to make way for development and their present location is unknown.

FOSTER FAMILY

William Foster and his wife Sarah settled along the Yuba River where the village of Foster's Bar is named for him. Because the killing of American Indians was not considered murder at that time, William was never tried for the deaths of Luis and Salvador during the Forlorn Hope.

GRAVES FAMILY

Franklin and Elizabeth Graves died in the mountains, but six of their eight children survived. Mary Ann Graves survived the Forlorn Hope and went on to become one of the first teachers in San Jose. In 1852, Nancy Graves joined the Methodist church and three years later she married a minister, Richard Williamson. They had nine children and eventually settled near Sebastopol, California. Her brother, William, who always held James Reed responsible for the tragedy, lectured frequently about the Donner party. Eleanor married in 1849 and had nine children.

REED FAMILY

Like the Breens, all of the Reed family members escaped the mountain disaster alive. They moved to San Jose where James Reed became a miner, rancher, and land developer who made a fortune in real estate speculation. He was active in civic affairs and briefly served as a sheriff and San Jose's chief

James and Margaret Reed enjoyed great success in California. Courtesy California State Parks. Sutter's Fort Archives

of police. Margaret never complained of migraine headaches again and nine months after they stumbled out of the mountains, she gave birth to a baby boy, Charles. Virginia was barely seventeen when she eloped with John M. Murphy, a U.S. Army officer who became wealthy in the gold rush. (Murphy was not related to the Murphys of the Donner party. He had arrived in California in 1844 with the Stephens party. Coincidentally, he had helped build the cabin used by the Reeds and Breens at Donner Lake.) Virginia Reed Murphy gave birth to nine children and lived to be eighty-seven years old. Martha "Patty" married Frank Lewis when she was eighteen and also had nine children. Reed later donated land that became the site of San Jose University and St. James Park. James Frazier Reed, who died at age 74 in 1874, never publicly mentioned killing John Snyder.

JOHN SUTTER

Swiss national John August Sutter arrived in Yerba Buena (San Francisco) in 1839. After negotiations with Mexican government officials, he acquired an enormous land grant of 48,000 acres at the junction of the Sacramento and American rivers. His trading post became the foundation for modern Sacramento. The gold discovered at his sawmill in January 1848 ultimately destroyed him. His workers deserted their posts and squatters overran his properties. Hordes of newcomers trampled his crops and slaughtered his livestock for food.

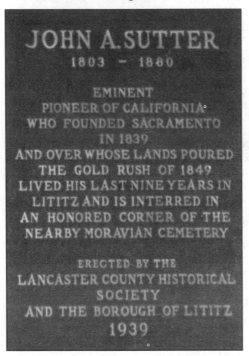

This historic plaque in Lititz, Pennsylvania, honors the legacy of John A. Sutter

Sutter, who more than any other person, had developed and promoted California's agricultural and mineral wealth, died destitute in a Pennsylvania hotel room. For fifteen years, Sutter petitioned Congress for $50,000 worth of restitution for the loss of his lands and the thousands of dollars that he had expended on arriving emigrants, but he was denied compensation.

Sutter chose Lititz, Pennsylvania, to build his home. The proximity to Washington, D.C. along with the reputed healing qualities of the nearby Lititz Springs appealed to the aging man. He also wanted his three grandchildren to have the benefits of the fine private and Moravian schools there.

Bones of Contention: Archaeology

On January 14, 2006, a Donner Party symposium was held during a national conference in Sacramento, hosted by the Society for Historical Archaeology. "The Donner Party: A Collaborative Approach" presentation provided an opportunity for about a dozen researchers and scientists to share with the media and public a fresh new look at this tragic western story.

Two days before the symposium, the co-directors involved in the Donner Party Archaeology Project (DPAP), Drs. Kelly Dixon and Julie Schablitsky, released preliminary data from recent excavations at one of the two winter encampments. The scientists said that if knife scarred bone fragments recovered from Alder Creek turned out to be human, it would be the first physical evidence of cannibalism in the Donner party.

After testing a few of the tiny fragments, however, they only identified cattle, horse, deer, dog, rabbit and rodent. The results were hardly sensational news, but indicative of the hyperbole that always seems to accompany anything related to the Donner party, the press release led to a nationally published Associated Press story with headlines like "Findings say Donner Party didn't resort to cannibalism" and "Lack of cooked bones at campsite a surprise."

The real story is that the analysis of a very small sampling of bone fragments from the Alder Creek location (only 30 out of about 16,000 pieces were tested) did not turn up any human bones, which is important, but does not prove definitively that the snowbound pioneers there did not resort to human flesh

Drs. Kelly Dixon (l) and Julie Schablitsky at Alder Creek dig. Photo by Bob Neyland

for food. The historical record documents rather conclusively that cannibalism did occur at the Donner Lake campsite, as well as at Alder Creek. The scientists involved in this on-going study made no such claims, yet the media headlines did, setting the stage for more confusion and misinformation, a problem which has plagued descendents and historians for 160 years.

Many books and historical accounts have been published about these California-bound emigrants, who were trapped east of the Sierra Nevada by early winter storms in 1846 and forced to eat the bodies of their dead. The research results presented at the symposium dispelled some of the myths and mysteries associated with the Donner family campsite, but the physical evidence fell short of answering many questions conclusively.

Archaeological research at the Donner encampments has been an ongoing process for decades. Co-leader of the DPAP

Dr. Kelly Dixon is an assistant professor of anthropology at the University of Montana, who specializes in historical archaeology of the American West. Dixon and her colleagues are following the work of professor Dr. Donald Hardesty, a University of Nevada-Reno anthropologist who led excavations at the Donner encampments in the 1980s and 1990s. At that time Hardesty proved that members of the Donner-led wagon train did camp at the east end of the lake. (The pioneers became separated upon their approach to the mountains and set up survival camps at different locations, best known as Donner Lake and Alder Creek.)

In the early 1990s, Dr. Hardesty excavated the ground at the base of the iconic "Donner tree" at Alder Creek, about six miles north of Donner Lake, but found little evidence that any pioneers had camped there for a prolonged period of time. The lack of artifacts forced historians and the Forest Service to acknowledge that

Chopped bone from Alder Creek. Photo by Julie Schablitsky

the revered tree did not indicate the location of the Donner campsite. Hardesty's frustrated crew expanded the search area and with the help of a metal detector survey soon discovered 19th century human artifacts about 200 yards away from the tree. Unfortunately, the project ran out of time and money before Hardesty could pursue the new leads, but his extensive research resulted in his book, *The Archaeology of the Donner Party*, published in 1997 by the University of Nevada Press.

Jump to the summers of 2003 and 2004, when Kelly Dixon and co-leader Julie Schablitsky, a historical archaeologist at the University of Oregon's Museum of Natural and Cultural

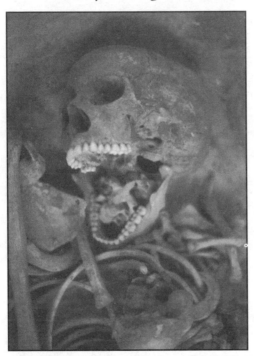

History, led a team of physical anthropologists and forensic specialists in researching whether the newly discovered campsite is truly that of the Donner families. The project was funded by The History Channel. Dixon had previously appeared in a Discovery Channel program "Unsolved History: The Donner Party."

During the recent Alder Creek digs, the team discovered the remains of a hearth, a very important find

3,000-year-old human skeleton in ancient Minoan crypt on Crete. Photo by Mark McLaughlin

because it suggests a long-term campsite. There were also pipe bowl fragments, bits of bone, including charred bone, lead balls and ceramic fragments. The artifacts were dated to the appropriate time period and the evidence of a fire hearth led the scientists to conclude that this indeed was most likely a Donner family campsite. Dr. Hardesty said, "This absolutely adds more credibility to the interpretation that this is where the Donner families camped," he said. "The artifacts they found are similar to what we found in 1990 and 1993."

New forensic technologies may lead the researchers into breakthrough territory. Schablitsky notes "Ten years ago, we didn't have the technology we have today. Ground-penetrating radar wasn't common and DNA analysis wasn't being used for archaeology. We can do so much more now."

Shannon Novak, an assistant professor of anthropology at Idaho State University, examined the bone fragments and found many of them were sawed, chopped and cut, "suggesting extreme desperation and starvation among the group." None of the fragments was over an inch in size; nearly 90% were smaller than ¼ inch. All of the bone found was calcined — cooked down to its mineral content. Calcined bone resists decomposition, but bone that retains its organic content readily dissolves in acidic soils like that at Alder Creek.

Alder Creek Valley looking east. Photo by Mark McLaughlin

There are limitations, however, to what the new skills and equipment can reveal. Nearly 16,000 bone fragments were recovered from the Alder Creek location, but virtually all of them are smaller than a fingernail in size. All of the pieces have suffered environmental degradation and many are too small to study effectively with current technologies. DNA analysis is unavailable due to the breakdown of the bone material due to temperature extremes, soil acidity, and a climate pattern of very wet and very dry conditions (winter vs. summer) at the site.

Scientists used scanning electron microscopes to study 30 of the larger pieces in a search for human bones that had been boiled (pot polish), an indicator of cannibalism. They were able to identify bones from horses, oxen, deer and dog, as well as rabbits and rodents, but no human bones were discovered. The variety of animal bones at the Alder Creek campsite does suggest that the stranded pioneers there may have had more food available than previously thought. The anthropologists involved in the study admit that based on the accounts that they had read, they definitely expected to find human remains among the animal bones, but to claim that no cannibalism occurred at the Alder Creek site based on these results is a conclusion that some find premature. The bones of the cannibalized bodies would not have been cooked repeatedly (flesh was cut from the corpse and cooked) and would not have survived the environmentally induced decomposition over 160 years.

Weather or Not: Historical Climatology 10

DONNER LAKE SNOW DEPTH IN 1847

The pedestal of the monument at Donner Memorial State Park is 22.5 feet high, which purportedly represents the maximum snow depth at Donner Lake during the winter of 1847. Was the snow really that deep? There are at least half a dozen historic photographs of cut tree stumps, but I could not find any image showing a cut stump exceeding 20 feet in height, including one that was probably located at Summit Valley, near 7,000 feet in elevation.

According to legend, Charles McGlashan, who contributed much to our understanding of what happened to the Donner Party, measured one cut stump at 22 feet, six inches in height. That apparent measurement was used for the monument. Research suggests, however, that the peak snow depth was less than 22.5 feet, probably somewhere between 15 to 20 feet deep at Donner Lake. Either way, the unfortunate emigrants were snowbound and unable to hunt because of the deep snowpack that winter.

EVIDENCE FOR 22.5-FOOT SNOW DEPTH AT DONNER LAKE

"Notwithstanding that the snowfall this year has been extraordinary, yet it is nothing compared to the winter when the Donner Party had their experience in this vicinity. G.W. Lyons, who is working in town, was a cousin to Mrs. Geo. Donner. He came to came to California in the summer of 1847 and from what the survivors of the Donner party told him he should judge that there had been twice as much snow

No matter how you cut it, the snow was deep. Courtesy U.S. Forest Service

that year as this. On the Marzen meadows were stumps of trees cut off 22 ft 6 inches from the ground. This would indicate nearly that depth of snow, which is twice the depth of this year. That winter was undoubtedly the most severe one on record." — *Truckee Republican* article reprinted in Tuscarora newspaper, Feb. 11, 1890. (Joe Marzen was a local butcher who owned the land where the Breen cabin stood and used it for cattle grazing.)

"One of the stumps near the Graves-Reed cabin, cut while the snow was at its deepest, was found by, by actual measurement, to be twenty-two feet in height. Part of this stump is standing today. The tall stumps have had a continuous tradition since the time of the Donner party disaster. The emigrant Lemuel McKeeby first noted them in 1849 — "Memoirs," *California Historical Society Quarterly*, 1924, III, p. 137.

"Several stumps were standing at Donner Lake in 1880 and of these two remained at the turn of the century. Others still stood in the more hospitable soil at the Alder Creek campsite as late as 1910, and three ancient specimens with well-defined undercuts, are still intact there." — Editor's notes, *History of the Donner Party* by McGlashan, 2nd edition, 1947, p. xxxvii, & p. 101.

"Visited Truckee Lake, half a mile above our camp. Near outlet of Lake were ruins of the cabins built by ill-fated Donner Party. Most of the cabins had been burned, and their charred remains, and whitened bones, half buried among withered pine leaves are sad memories of the event. Also tall stumps, some 20 feet high, showing the trees were cut, gave an idea of the great depth of snow." — John Steele (1850).

"It is hardly necessary to remark that no relics have ever been found under the site of the Murphy cabin. The tall stumps which surround this rock, and the site of the Graves and Reed cabin, and which are particularly numerous around the site of

The monument's pedestal at Donner Memorial State Park is 22.5 feet high, and, according to legend, represents the maximum snow depth at Donner Lake that winter. Trees dwarf the monument and the monument dwarfs visitors. Photo by Mark McLaughlin

the Donner tents at Alder Creek, are of themselves remarkable relics. Many of them were cut by a person who stood on the top of very deep snow. They are frequently ten, fifteen, and twenty feet in height. Time and action of the elements have caused them to decay until, in some instances, a child's hand might cause them to totter and fall. In a few years more they all will have disappeared." — Charles F. McGlashan, *History of the Donner Party*, Stanford University Press, 1880, 2d edition, 1947.

"This projection brought the total height of the pedestal [Donner monument] to 22.5 feet, the height of the snow of 1846." — Doris Foley, *The Pioneer [Donner] Monument: The Origin of a Statue*, Searles Historical Library, Nevada City, 1982, p. 17.

Scientists at the Central Sierra Snow Laboratory examine snowpack hydrology. Photo by Randall Osterhuber

EVIDENCE AGAINST 22.5-FOOT SNOW DEPTH AT DONNER LAKE

Patrick Breen kept a diary from Nov. 20, 1846, until March 1, 1847. In it he gave a first-hand account of the weather at Donner Lake and some of the daily events. It is one of the most remarkable documents of the American West. In general, Sierra snow depths fluctuate greatly during the winter months, but on January 13, Breen wrote, "Snow higher than the shanty, must be 13 feet deep." Heavy snow fell later in the month and on Feb. 1, Breen observed, "The snow has not settled much." From Feb. 4 - 6 Breen says about six more feet of snow fell. The peak snow depth was probably somewhere between 15 to 20 feet deep at Donner Lake.

"The stumps of fallen trees near the front of the cabins, stand at the height of 5 & 10 feet, some probably over the latter, showing the depth of the snow when the trees were fallen for firewood. The donor [Donner] cabins stood 200 yards above the road & some distance from the Lake. Their remains or ashes & the bottom logs are only to be seen to designate to the passing traveler the spot where the painful sufferings occurred...'"
— Augustus Ripley Burbank, September 10, 1849

"The stumps of the trees cut by the party still stand, and are from fifteen to eighteen feet in height, showing the great depth to which the cabins and all in the camp lay buried."
— Dan De Quille, *The Big Bonanza*

"Tall stumps, for example, are also found in other parts of the Sierra Nevada, especially in the Carson Range, and are associated with winter logging in the 1860s and 1870s." — Donald Hardesty, *The Archaeology of the Donner Party*, p. 115.

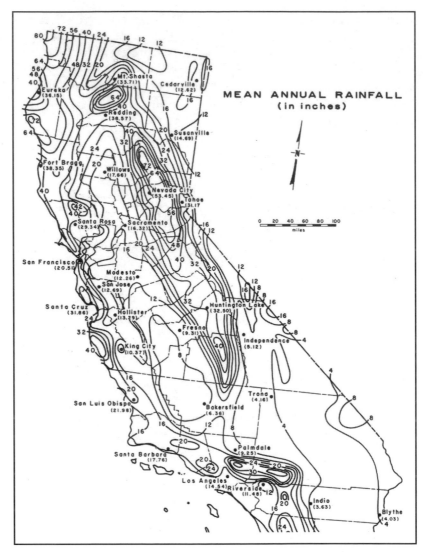

California's Mean Annual Rainfall. Isohyetal maps use contour lines to express equal amounts of rainfall. Courtesy National Weather Service

CONTEMPORARY COMMENTS ABOUT 1847 WINTER

"The rainy season set in the year I was there [1846] on the 29th of October and continued to rain at intervals up to the last of May in a few instances it rained two and three days and nights and then cleared off with as beautiful weather as I ever beheld and by a reference to my Journal I find that near two thirds of the winter was clear pleasant weather." — Letter by John Craig, October 4, 1847. "Overland in 1846" Vol. 1, p. 139)

"This last winter [1846-47] is the coldest ever been known in California....we walked on snow shoes over the snow it was from 5 to 25 feet deep." — Daniel Rhoads (Letter to his father-in-law, Jesse Esrey, written in summer of 1847. Rhoads was a member of the First Relief Party.)

"The [Sierra] snow was from 5 to 30 feet deep." -- Lilburn W. Boggs letter written to Alphonso Boone in early April 1847, published in the *Oregon Spectator* on July 8, 1847. (*Unfortunate Emigrants*, Edited by Kristin Johnson, pg. 125)

"The writer who is well qualified to judge, is of the opinion that the whole party might have reached the California valley before the first fall of snow, if the men had exerted themselves as they should have done." — George McKinstry, *California Star*.

"The winter of 1846 was one of the severest rainy seasons that had visited the coast for years. We had a repetition of some of its hardships in 1849." — Edward C. Kemble

May 1, 1847 Donner Pass: "On the first day of May we succeeded in crossing the main summit of the California mountains or the Sierra Nevada the snow being from 3 to 8 feet deep on the western slope, but on turning down the Eastern side it was perhaps from 8 to 20 or even 30 feet deep

Strong southwest winds transport additional snow to the lee side of Sierra ridges. This frozen wave was photographed in July 1995. Photo by Mark McLaughlin

owing to the wind being always from the southwest when the snow is falling and carrying large quantities from the western side which is deposited on the east side. — James Clyman, *Journal of a Mountain Man*, 1984 reprint

June 7, 1847 Donner Pass: "On my return home I supplied myself with seven mules with packs and all things necessary and in company with seven others we started for home [Ogden, Utah], on June 2. On the fifth day we crossed the peak of the California mountains and had to travel about 35 miles over snow varying from 5 to 20 feet deep and rode over numerous mountain streams on arches of snow whilst we could hear the water roaring and dashing under our feet." — John Craig (*Salt Desert Trails* by Charles Kelly, Western Epics, Inc., Salt Lake City, 1996, p. 121)

"Some modern critics have maintained that their disaster [Donner] resulted from their attempting Donner Pass instead of the Coldstream Canyon route, but the original documents give no such indication. If the alternate route offered easier grades, it crossed at a higher altitude and was also longer, and there is no reason to think that by attempting it they would have done any better. Once blocked by the snow, most of the emigrants displayed as much energy and initiative as could be expected, as is shown by the numerous attempts to escape across the pass on foot. But their failure to watch their cattle was unfortunate." — George Stewart, *Donner Pass*

T.H. Jefferson published a California Trail map in early 1849. Jefferson advised that pioneers who arrived late and found snow on Donner Pass should return back to the desert (Reno) — "The most difficult portion of the whole journey is the passage of the Californian Mountains, and particularly the descent of the western side. The only serious difficulty, however, is when you arrive late in the season, with a short supply of breadstuff, and encounter snow ten or fifteen feet deep. Those who expect to cross in safety must reach the Truckey Pass by the 1st of October. The snow does not usually begin falling till November, and remains upon the ground more or less till May. If you arrive late, however, and encounter snow, do not attempt to cross the mountain, but scatter at once into small parties, and retreat to the eastern base of the mountains, where you will find fertile valleys free from snow, which afford game, salmon, and roots, enough for small parties. You can winter there, and cross at the Truckey Pass when the snow is gone." — Dale Morgan, *Overland in 1846* Vol. 1, p. 243

"Such a state of things will probably never again occur, from the fact, that the road is now better known, and the emigrants will hereafter start and travel so as to cross the mountain by the 1st of October. The [Donner] party which are suffering so much, lost their work cattle on the salt plains, on Hastings' Cut off, a route which we hope no one will ever attempt again." — Monterey *Californian*

EVIDENCE FOR A DRY WINTER

"Lake levels of the Great Basin of Nevada and eastern Oregon were also somewhat low during most of the 1840s and generally increased after. Tree rings indicate that drought was more frequent for most areas in the Intermountain West during the 1840s, particularly in eastern Oregon and eastern Nevada." — *Meteorological Experiences, Climatic Variability, and Overland Trail Emigrants*

Dendrochronology is the science of climate reconstruction by studying tree rings. Each year a tree adds a layer of wood to its trunk and branches thus creating the annual rings dendro-

The tree ring analysis of these stumps in the Walker River indicate they grew during a century long drought. Photo by Mark McLaughlin

chronologists see when they study a cross section. New wood grows from the cambium layer between the old wood and the bark. The amount of new growth corresponds to the amount of precipitation received in the region.

Scientists at the Laboratory of Tree-Ring Research, University of Arizona in Tucson, developed a tree-ring chronology of California in the 1980s. There were four types of trees used in this study, selected at a variety of sites in California and the west, including one on Donner Summit. The California sites were located within or close to the Sacramento Basin. These data were applied to the reconstruction of river flows, including the Sacramento, Feather, Yuba and American, which drain the northern Sierra Nevada. Low flow years in the region's river drainages included 1843-50 (Sacramento) and 1843-48 (American), which suggests below average precipitation during the winter of 1846-47. In fact, all of the four rivers indicated below normal water flow in 1847. As a result of this study, seasonal precipitation for the Sierra Nevada during the winter of 1847 is estimated at 80% to near normal. — *Reconstructing Riverflow in the Sacramento Basin since 1560.*

Precipitation, however, is different than snowfall. Precipitation represents rain combined with snow that has been melted for its water content. It is possible that members of the Donner Party experienced a heavy snow year, even if tree ring studies show the winter below normal. For example, the snowiest winter near Donner Pass (measurements began in 1879) was 1937-38 when 819 inches were recorded. But that

Deep snow during the winter of 1938 at Homewood on Lake Tahoe's west shore. Courtesy Bill Callender

winter only ranks 26th on the all-time precipitation list because the abundant snow that fell that year had relatively little moisture. I suspect that in 1938, and possibly in 1847, the most significant storm events were cold (Gulf of Alaska origin) and the snow often dry and powdery. Dry snow has greater loft and will measure deeper than wet snow.

Example: A Pacific storm may generate one inch of water during its passage. If the storm is cold, more snowfall will

be measured than if it is warm, even though the same one-inch of precipitation will have fallen. Sierra snowstorms average about a 1:12 ratio, meaning that for every inch of water about one foot of snow will fall. A lower ratio than that makes for relatively wet snow, often called "Sierra cement." However, if the storm is cold enough, that ratio can climb to 1:18, and sometimes greater, meaning that 18 inches or more snowfall will be measured for every inch of precipitation. The

Fifteen-foot snowpack at Soda Springs in March 1983. Courtesy Richard Steinheimer & Shirley Burman

Wasatch Mountains in Utah commonly get snowfalls in the 1:20 ratio and greater, thus earning their mountain resorts the bragging rights of great skiing in "champagne powder."

It is possible, even likely considering the eye witness accounts, that cold temperatures and low snow levels during the winter of 1847 produced significant snowfall at Donner Lake and Alder Creek, as well as a hefty snowpack in the higher elevations. With low water content in the snow, however, the tree ring representing that season will indicate a below average or near normal water year. Regardless, as Donald Hardesty writes in his book, *The Archaeology of the Donner Party*, "All in all, however, it is clear that early fall snows played a key role in the tragedy, whatever the winter as a whole may have been like."

EVIDENCE FOR A WET WINTER

In a remarkable contradiction to the California tree ring chronologies, climate reconstructions of lake levels in Nevada, first published in 1941, indicate precipitation in the Pyramid and Winnemucca lake watersheds 180% of average during 1847. Lake level histories of the Great Basin can be found in "A 100 Years Record of Truckee River Runoff Estimated from Changes in the Levels and Volumes of Pyramid and Winnemucca Lakes." — *Transactions of the American Geophysical Union*, 1941.

"During the past week a succession of showers, sufficient to moisten the earth—the annual "May rains;" none to come after. San Joaquin country flooded; unusual amount of rain on the mountains in winter." — Dr. Henry Gibbons, M.D., from *California Star* (May 8, 1847, San Francisco) [Dr. Gibbons arrived in San Francisco in 1850 by ship. He had been a weather observer in Philadelphia and Wilmington, Delaware, since the 1820s. Dr. Gibbons was a "highly regarded and prominent citizen, and was noted for his investigations into the climate of San Francisco and California." — David Ludlum]

During the winter of 1890, thousands of men were hired to shovel the railroad tracks over Donner Pass. Courtesy Nevada Historical Society

"Considerable rain; crops good." — A. Campbell (Campbell compiled information on historic wet and dry years for southern California. He considered the winter of 1847 wet.)

Los Angeles rainfall: Calendar year 1846 – 10.45 inches: Year 1847 – 20.15 inches

"The winter of 1846 was one of the severest rainy seasons that had visited the coast for years. We had a repetition of some of its hardships in 1849." — Edward C. Kemble [Kemble arrived in Yerba Buena at age 17 in 1846. Several winters preceding his arrival were drier than normal, thus the rains of 1846–47 could have easily been considered exceptional.]

HISTORY OF WEATHER OBSERVATIONS

The history of early meteorological observations in the Far West is closely connected with that of its exploration by

Europeans. Non-instrumental weather observations date back to September 1542, when Cabrillo entered San Diego Bay, and wrote the following in his log book, "A very great gale blew from the southwest; the port being good, we felt nothing." Cabrillo explored the coast as far north as southern Oregon, but the coasts of northern Oregon and Washington were unseen by Europeans until the explorations of Perez and Heceta in 1774-75. Colonization in California started in 1769 with the establishment of a mission and presidio at San Diego.

In the Pacific Northwest, trading posts appeared towards the end of the 18th century. In 1792, the mouth of the Columbia River was discovered, and 13 years later, the overland expedition under Lewis and Clark built Fort Clatsop in its vicinity.

The first regular weather observations in the Far West were made at Fort Clatsop, between November 14, 1805, and March 23, 1806, and consisted of daily entries of wind direction, and occurrence of fog, clouds, rain, hail and thunder: no temperature was recorded as the only thermometer was lost in September. The next regular observations were made at Astoria, Oregon, where a gentleman who resided at the fort took daily temperature observations three times a day from 1821 to 1824.

The first mention of meteorological observations in the San Francisco area appeared in the accounts of exploring and trading expeditions of European ships during the early part of the 19th century. The first instrumental weather observations appear to have been taken by Captain Beechey at Yerba Buena (San Francisco), in November and December 1826. Capt. Beechey arrived at New Albion (Bodega Bay) on Nov. 5, 1826, and departed Monterey on January 5, 1827. A detailed diary was kept not only of temperature and occurrence of precipitation, but also of atmospheric pressure, tides and magnetic variations. — *Narrative of a Voyage to the Pacific and Bering's Strait,"* Captain Frederick William Beechey, London, 1831.

In 1812, the Russians established Ross, California, and occupied it until 1841. Weather observations were made at this fort and at Rancho Chernykh, about nine miles inland, between January 1837 and March 1839, consisting of thrice daily temperature observations as well as those of atmospheric pressure, sky cover, rain, fog, hail and thunder. The original thermometer was exposed on the north side of a building near the seashore, where it was protected from direct sunlight and was openly exposed to the prevailing westerly winds. It was originally recorded in degrees Reaumur. On the Reaumur scale water freezes at zero degrees and boils at 80 degrees.

Nineteenth century pioneer weather observers.
Harper's Illustrated Weekly

No regular weather observations in the Far West appear to have been made between 1841 and 1846. The years were turbulent politically as large-scale overland migration brought friction or war with Indians, Mexicans and Englishmen. The northern boundary of the western United States was established in 1846 by the treaty of Ghent, and the southern one in 1848 by the treaty of Guadalupe Hidalgo. Meteorological observations were started at Presidio San Francisco and Presidio Monterey, California in April 1847 by the U.S. Army Medical Department. These two stations were the only ones in California until the summer of 1849 when regular mail service was established with the east (by ship and carriers via Panama) and temperature records began in San Francisco, San Diego and Sacramento. (No thermometer readings appear in the records of the Franciscan missionaries.)

The surgeon at each post was required to keep a "Diary of the Weather," employing a thermometer and a rain gauge. Some of the early records prior to March 1850 have not been preserved, but thereafter they are continuous. The place of observations was at Fort Point on the south shore of the Golden Gate, so the records are not comparable with those taken in downtown San Francisco.

San Francisco Snowstorms

During the second week of March 1847, naval surgeon Dr. Marius Duvall was stationed aboard the American war-ship *Portsmouth*, anchored in Monterey Bay. His observations indicated an exceptionally cold storm raging over California. "The last few days the [weather] has been excessively cold, and is disposed to continue so." he wrote. "The hills near here are covered with snow, and last night some fell in town." Hail fell in San Francisco that week and high temperatures were only about 40 degrees. Snow is relatively rare on the California coast, but a brief look at San Francisco's climate history illustrates that it does occur on occasion.

San Francisco's location in the middle latitudes and right on the California coast places it in a Mediterranean climate zone characterized by moist mild winters and dry summers. Snowstorms in downtown San Francisco are rare; in fact, during the last 150 years there have been only six documented

U.S. Pacific fleet enters San Francisco Bay, circa 1960. Courtesy U.S. Navy

snowfall events with one inch or more measured in that district. Snow accumulates more frequently and to greater depths on the surrounding hills, but the inner city itself is almost always spared the winter coat of white. (The last time San Francisco's financial district received an inch of snow was December 11, 1932.)

Captain F. W. Beechey who sailed to San Francisco Bay in the 1820s observed snow and frost in the area. "We nevertheless saw hoarfrost upon the grass in the mornings [1827], and in the following year observed snow lie several hours upon the ground [in Yerba Buena]. The third of December [1827] we left the harbor of San Francisco, the shores of which, being newly clothed with snow, had a very wintry appearance."

French explorer, Count Eugene Duflot de Mofras, explored the Oregon and California coasts in 1844. He wrote, "Snow falls in large quantities on the Sierra Nevada every winter and lies until summer; and so too on the summits of the Coast Range in the northern part of the State. On the peak of Mount Diablo and some of the highest peaks southward there are one or two slight falls nearly every winter; but the snow lies only for a day or two. At San Francisco and in the valleys in generally, except at rare intervals many years apart, the ground is never whitened. In January 1806, snow fell at the mission of San Juan Bautista; but it was the only time for 70 years up to 1842." Duflot de Mofras also stated that thunder was so rare in California that the Indians had no word to express the phenomenon. — *Explorations de l'Oregon et des Californies*, Paris, 1844, p. 47

Colder weather and coastal snowfall events were more common in California during the 19th century than they are today. In the days before the automobile, when urbanites walked or rode the trolley, newspaper accounts rendered a pleasing picture of appreciation for that rare meteorological event, a real San Francisco snowstorm.

On December 30, 1856, a two and a half inch snowfall added to the city's holiday cheer. The *Alta California* reported; "The oldest inhabitant was about the streets yesterday, freely expressing his opinion that he had never seen such a day before in San Francisco. For several hours together, the white feathery flakes, such as in the Eastern States when they cover the ground with a snowy mantle, bring out the prancing horses and merry faces whose laugh keeps time to the music of the jingling sleigh bells — just such snow, the pure and genuine article, fell yesterday in San Francisco. The thermometer, during the day, fell very low; at one time in the afternoon, it sunk to 36 degrees, an unusual temperature for San Francisco."

Today, most scientists take the threat of global warming and climate change very seriously. Climate change was on some people's minds in the 19th century too. In 1856, an *Alta California* editor noted: "Are the seasons changing with the innovations which the Anglo Saxon race has made in California? We shall begin to think so if we continue having snow storms in winter and rains in July." In the mid 1850s, there was a whimsical notion among native Californians that "…the coming of 'these Yankee devils' has completely changed the character of the seasons here, the winter months especially being, it is believed, now wetter and colder than before the American advent." — *Annals of San Francisco*, 1855, p. 514.

Several individuals recorded temperature and precipitation in San Francisco before the advent of the U.S. Weather Service, the most noted being Thomas Tennent from Philadelphia. Tennent, who designed nautical and mathematical instruments, began taking daily measurements on August 14, 1849, shortly after his arrival in San Francisco. The Army Signal Service took over observations on March 1, 1871, but due to Tennent's expertise as an instrument maker and the fact that he recorded rainfall to the nearest 100th of an inch, his data were accepted as the "official" early record. (Note: Virtually all of the original 19th century California weather records and documents were destroyed in the 1906 quake-fire, but many were later reconstituted by incorporating previously published data from journals and newspapers.)

A snowstorm on January 12, 1868, inspired the *Alta California* to remark; "Snow covered all the roofs and sidewalks even in the lower part of town, and the hills were for the first time in years completely whitened. The effect produced upon the city was to us in California startlingly beautiful. The velvet coating of the snow on the outlines of roofs, towers, gables and steeples with sharp distinctness, and the hills beyond the Mis-

San Francisco snowstorm at corner of Market and Post streets, December 31, 1882. Courtesy Bancroft Library

sion Dolores, and so on all around the Bay of San Francisco were as white as the Alps in midwinter. Thus far the winter has been a rough one throughout the State, and it is likely to be long remembered as such by everybody in California."

During the 1880s, a decade when wintry storms plagued the continental U.S., San Francisco residents experienced four winter seasons with snow; 1882, 1884, 1887, and 1888. On New Years Eve, 1882, steady snow fell for 5 hours, reaching 3.5 inches deep in the downtown area. Large crowds of boys and girls gathered to build snowmen and throw snowballs. Telephone and telegraph service were interrupted because of downed wires, and the flower beds and exotic gardens in Golden Gate Park were damaged by the thick blanket of ice. A two-inch snowfall graced the city on February 7, 1884, but it was hardly noticed by the bustling metropolis. It seemed that the city's residents were getting used to winter snowstorms. But three years later, when half of foot fell, the town went crazy.

San Francisco's all-time record snowfall occurred on February 5, 1887, when 3.7 inches were measured at the downtown weather bureau location in the financial district. At higher elevations in the western portion of the city, the snow was 7 inches deep. The snowdepth at California Street and Central Avenue was measured at just over 6 inches. The *San Francisco Chronicle* devoted five full columns to accounts of the historic storm. The newspaper waxed poetically on the bucolic scene; "The first broad flakes came softly down

San Francisco's record snowstorm on Taylor Street, February 5, 1887. Courtesy Bancroft Library

a few minutes before 3 o'clock yesterday morning and settled as lightly as swan's down on the dark earth. People from the East saw again the Christmas of their youth, and the little ones went wild to find that their experience of snow was not to be confined to storybooks."

The *Chronicle* noted the excitement of little children with the novel appearance of snow: "There was an especial poetry about the joys of the little ones. There was not one who could toddle who did not rush into the streets to romp in the white, and even the sick children were carried to the windows, that they might see how bravely Mother Goose was shaking the feathers down." But it was not total bliss throughout the city. The *Chronicle* reported "...the street-car men journeyed up and down their lines, running the gauntlet of hundreds of men and boys who did not content themselves with snowballs, but flung hard, sharp ice, and acted as maliciously as fiends. The streetcars were pelted with snowballs without mercy, and much glass was broken. By noon, however, the small boys had been confined to the house to dry his clothes and the trainmen were less annoyed."

The paper also mentioned; "A number of former residents of Albany, New York, made a large toboggan and named it the 'Major Macfarlane,' after the editor of the Albany *Press*. Yesterday morning Thomas Doolan was elected Captain and Judge Pennie steersman, and a trial run was made down Haight Street hill. This is probably the first toboggan club organized in California, and the members send greetings to the coasting clubs of New York State!"

CLIMATE AND HEALTH

For many of the emigrants traveling the California Trail in 1846, a common reason for heading west was to improve their health. That included members of the Donner Party. In his 1845 pioneers guidebook, *The Emigrant's Guide to Oregon and California*, promoter Lansford Hastings described California as if it were a biblical Garden of Eden. He painted a picture of an idyllic landscape blessed by perfect weather. He promised, "There will be no land on earth that can compare with California with respect to its wonderful climate, the excellent health of its inhabitants." The rhetoric would certainly have appealed to George Donner, a father of five young children and no "spring chicken" in 1846.

Hastings also claimed, "No fires are required, at any season of the year, in parlors, offices or ships, hence fuel is never required, for any other than culinary purposes. It may be truly said of this country [California], "December is as pleasant as May. The remarks are applicable only to the valleys and plains, for the mountains present but one eternal winter. Hence it is seen, that you may here enjoy perennial spring, or perpetual winter at your option."

Marketing California's "perfect climate." Author's collection

James Reed's wife, Margaret, suffered from chronic headaches and 57-year-old Franklin Ward Graves was probably attracted to the region for health and aging issues. George Donner, age 62, and his brother Jake, in his mid 50s, may have been thinking along the same lines. It is said that Edwin Bryant, an editor of the Louisville *Courier — Journal*, was inspired to head west because of his failing health. Bryant, who spent about ten months in California from 1846 to 1847, later wrote, "For salubrity I do not think there is any climate in the world superior to that of the coast of California. I was in the country nearly a year, exposed much of the time to great hardships and privations, sleeping, for the most part, in the open air, and I never felt while there the first

To reach California's mild climate, westbound motorists must deal with Sierra snow. Photo circa July 1952. Courtesy North Lake Tahoe Historical Society

pang of disease, or the slightest indication of bad health. There is but little disease in the country arising from the climate."

Luke Halloran, who the Donner's had taken into their care near Fort Bridger, was heading for California to cure his affliction of tuberculosis. Even the mountain man James Clyman, who had tried to warn the Donner Party off of the Hastings' cutoff, had moved west because he was "troubled by a cough."

Early emigrants drawn to California were inspired by economic opportunity and free land, but there is no doubt the lure of better health was a major factor. One of the tragic ironies associated with the Donner Party is that the attraction of a life free of disease in the "salubrious and healthful climate" of California was one of the reasons for the journey west. For nearly half of the members, however, that dream was preempted by severe winter weather and starvation. You might say that the coastal climate lured them, but the mountain weather killed them. Author Robert Heinlein wrote, "Climate is what you expect, weather is what you get."

For years, health-seeking immigrants were inspired by reports that California's climate was so perfect that disease was non-existent. In his 1836 book, *Two Years Before the Mast*, Richard Henry Dana wrote that California was "blessed with a climate which there can be no better in the world; free from all manner of diseases, whether epidemic or endemic..."

In his 19th century book, *The Mediterranean Shores of America; Southern California*, Dr. Peter C. Remondino stated, "From my personal observations, I can say that at least an extra 10 years' lease on life is gained by a removal to this coast from the Eastern States; not 10 years to be added with its extra weight of age and infirmity, but 10 years more with additional benefit of feeling 10 years younger during the time."

In the early 1870s, the Los Angeles City Chamber of Commerce began a climate promotion campaign to draw immigrants to the region. Health and longevity were trumpeted to easterners and Europeans. One advertisement boasted, "We sell the climate at so much per acre and throw in the land; it's $10 for an acre of land, and $490 an acre for the climate."

Antoine Robidoux visited California before the 1849 Gold Rush. Upon his return to Missouri, Robidoux began giving talks in which he praised the virtues of the California climate. He is reported to have told a group of listeners that, "There never was but one man in California who had the chills. He was from Missouri and carried the disease in his system. It was such a curiosity to see a man shake with the chills that the people of Monterey went eighteen miles into the country to see him."

One of my favorite stories about the health benefits associated with the California climate is the story about a man from Missouri who had moved to California in the gold rush. When he had become an old man, he decided that he wanted to visit the "old country" to see his family and friends one last time. While in Missouri, he contracted one of the deadly diseases common in the region at that time and the doctor told him he was about to die. Before he succumbed to the disease, he made his friends promise that they would take his body back to California so he could be buried in his adopted state. A coffin was constructed and the deceased Californian was loaded into a wagon for the trip west. A month later, imagine everyone's surprise when, after they had buried him in a coastal cemetery, their dead comrade popped up alive, resurrected by the Golden State's salubrious climate and rich soil!

Donner Summit Maximum Snow Depths of record: (Central Sierra Snow Lab)

Elevation 6,900 feet: Avg. annual snowfall 410 inches (34.2 ft.)

March 3, 1938: 12 feet

March 28, 1952: 15.7 feet (Lake Lucille, 8,200 ft., 20.3 feet)

March 4, 1969: 15.9 feet (Lake Lucille, 8,200 ft., 21.6 feet)

March 28, 1983: 15.7 feet (Meadow Lake – Yuba River, 7,200 ft., 19.2 feet)

Donner Lake Maximum Snow Depths of record: (U.S. Forest Service)

Elevation 5,937 feet: Avg. annual snowfall 183 inches (15.3 ft)

Feb. 27, 1969: 9.6 feet (Donner Memorial State Park)

In early March 1969, the Donner monument marker was about half buried by snow. In the next few days, newspapers kept the public abreast of the fact that snow was reaching unprecedented levels in the Sierra. The 14.5 feet of snow at Truckee was said to be the greatest of any station along the northern edge of Tahoe. Snow levels at Donner Park approached record levels (according to Soil Conservation Service), but snow measurements have been taken at Donner Lake only since 1959. Official snow depth measurements there include 62 inches (5.2 feet) in Feb. 1967; 74 inches (6.2 feet) in March 1959; and 79 inches (6.6 feet) in April 1962.

Alder Creek Maximum Snow Depths of record: (Sagehen Creek Field Station Data)

March 31, 1952: 9.4 feet (Sagehen Creek Snow Survey, 6,500 ft.)

March 1969: 13 feet (Sagehen Creek Field Station, 6,390 ft.)

March 1969: 10.4 feet (To estimate snow depth at Alder Creek at 5,800 ft., 20% was subtracted from the Sagehen Creek data.)

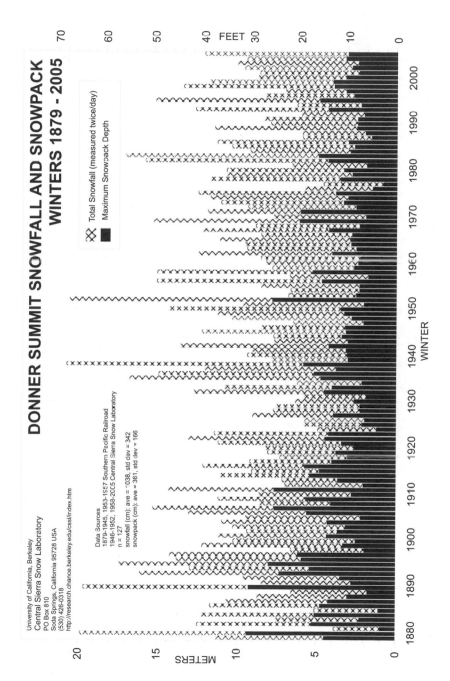

Snowfall chart courtesy Randall Osterhuber

SELECTED SOURCES & BIBLIOGRAPHY

Research for Weathering the Storm *included numerous newspaper and magazine articles, as well as many interviews and discussions with Donner Party descendants and various experts in the field. A selected list of relevant non-fiction source material is provided below for the interested reader.*

Baucr, K. Jack. *The Mexican War: 1846-1848.* (University of Nebraska Press, Lincoln & London, 1974).

Bryant, Edwin. *What I Saw in California* (1848). (University of Nebraska Press, Lincoln and London, 1985). First published in 1848 by D. Appleton & Company.

Calabro, Marian. *The Perilous Journey of the Donner Party.* (Clarion Books, New York, N.Y., 1999).

Clyman, James. *Journal of a Mountainman.* Mountain Press Publishing Company, Missoula, Montana, 1984.

Cordine, John. Graciously provided microfilm of deck logs of the sloops *Portsmouth* and *Warren.*

De Quille, Dan. *The Big Bonanza.* Alfred A. Knopf, New York, 1876. Reprint 1947.

De Voto, Bernard. *The Year of Decision 1846.* (The American Heritage Library, Houghton Mifflin Company, Boston, 1942 & 1984).

Dillon, Richard. *Captain John Sutter: Sacramento Valley's Sainted Sinner.* (Western Tanager, Santa Cruz, California, 1967).

Duvall, Marius. *A Navy Surgeon in California 1847-1847: The Journal of Marius Duvall.* (John Howell, San Francisco, 1957).

Earle, Christopher J. & Fritts, Harold C. *Reconstructing Riverflow in the Sacramento Basin Since 1560.* California Dept. of Water Resources, 1986.

Farnham, Eliza, W. Narrative of the Emigration of the Donner Party to California in 1846, in *California, In-Doors and Out.* (New York, N.Y. 1856).

Felton, Ernest L. *California's Many Climates: Where to Live in California.* (Pacific Books, Publisher, Palo Alto, California, 1965.)

Gill, Richardson B. *The Great Maya Droughts: Water, Life, and Death.* (University of New Mexico Press, Albuquerque, 2000).

Graydon, Charles K. *Trail of the First Wagons Over the Sierra Nevada.* (The Patrice Press, St. Louis, Missouri, 1986).

Grayson, Donald K. *The Deserts Past.* Chapter Ten:" Historic Archaeology and the Donner Party" and "Donner Party Deaths: A Demographic Assessment." *Journal of Anthropological Research,* 1990. Grayson is an archaeologist with the University of Washington.

Hardesty, Donald L. *Archaeology of the Donner Party.* (University of Nevada Press, Reno, 1997).

Harding, Sidney T. *Recent Variations in the Water Supply of the Western Great Basin.* (University of California Press, Berkeley, Los Angeles & London, 1965).

Harlow, Neal. *California Conquered: The Annexation of a Mexican Province 1846-1850.* (University of California Press, Berkeley, Los Angeles & London, 1982).

Hastings, Lansford Warren. *The Emigrant's Guide to Oregon and California.* (Applewood Books; Bedford, Massachusetts; 1845). Reprint.

Houghton, Eliza P. Donner. *The Expedition of the Donner Party and Its Tragic Fate.* (A. C. McClurg & Co., Chicago, 1911. Reprint 1996 by the Sierra District of California State Parks).

Howard, Thomas Frederick. *Sierra Crossing: First Roads to California.* (University of California Press, Berkeley, Los Angeles & London, 1998).

Johnson, Kristin. *Unfortunate Emigrants: Narratives of the Donner Party.* (Utah State University Press, Logan, Utah, 1996).

Johnson, Kristin. "Donner Party Bulletin: Alder Creek Issue." Issue No. 15, January 31, 2006. See Johnson's website: www.utahcrossroads.org

Kelly, Charles. *Salt Desert Trails.* ((Western Epics, Inc., Salt Lake City, Utah, 1996).

Klieforth, Harold & Powell, Douglas. *Sierra East: Edge of the Great Basin*. Chapter Four: Weather and Climate. (California Natural History Guides, University of California Press, Berkeley & Los Angeles, 2000).

Kimble, Edward Cleveland. *A Kemble Reader: Stories of California, 1846-1848*. (The California Historical Society, San Francisco, 1963).

King, Joseph A. *Winter of Entrapment — Revised Edition*. (K&K Publications, Lafayette, California, 1994).

Limburg, Peter R. *Deceived: The Story of the Donner Party*. (International Publishing Services, Pacifica, California, 1998).

Mathers, James. *Journey of travels from Missouri to California 1846*. Published in Dale Morgan's *Overland in 1846*: Volume 1. (University of Nebraska Press, Lincoln & London, 1963).

McCurdy, MD, Stephen A. *Epidemiology of disaster: The Donner Party (1846-1847)*. (University of California, Davis; School of Medicine Medical Journal, 1990, 160:338-342).

McLaughlin, Mark. *Weather Analysis of 1846-1847*. (Unpublished). Research paper presented January 14, 2006, at Society for Historical Archaeology (SHA) Conference for Donner Party Archaeology Project in Sacramento, California.

McGlashan, Charles F. *History of the Donner Party*. (Stanford University Press, Stanford, California, 1880. Reprinted 1947).

McGlashan, Nona M. & Betty H. *From the Desk of Truckee's C.F. McGlashan*. (Truckee Donner Historical Society, Panorama West Books, Fresno, California).

Mergen, Bernard. *Snow in America*. (Smithsonian Institution Press, Washington and London, 1997).

Mock, Cary J. & Lawson, Marlin P. *Meteorological Experiences, Climatic Variability, and Overland Trail Emigrants*.(Journal of the West, Vol. 40, #3, Summer 2001).

Morgan, Dale, *Overland in 1846: Diaries and Letters of the California Trail*, Vols. I & II. (University of Nebraska Press, London & Lincoln, 1963).

Morgan, Dale L. & Korns, J. Roderic. *West from Fort Bridger: The Pioneering of Immigrant Trails across Utah, 1846-1850.* Revised and Updated by Will Bagley & Harold Schindler. (Utah State University Press, Logan, Utah, 1994).

Mullen, Jr., Frank X. *The Donner Party Chronicles.* (Nevada Humanities Committee, Reno, 1997).

Murphy, Virginia Reed. *Across the Plains in the Donner Party: A Personal Narrative of the Overland Trip to California 1846-47.* (Outbooks, Inc., Golden, Colorado, 1980).

Nordhoff, Charles. *California: For Health, Pleasure, and Residence; A Book for Travelers and Settlers.* (New York, 1873).

Osterhuber, Randall S. *Climatic Summary of Donner Summit*, California. Central Sierra Snow Laboratory, October 1993.

Reed, James S. *An Analysis of the Psychological, Emotional, and Spiritual States of the Donner Party.* Research paper presented January 14, 2006, at Society for Historical Archaeology (SHA) Conference for Donner Party Archaeology Project in Sacramento, California.

Sherwood, Midge. *Frémont: Eagle of the West.* (Jackson Peak Publishers, North Hollywood, California, 2002).

Steed, Jack. *The Donner Party Rescue Site: Johnson's Ranch on Bear River.* (Graphic Publishers, Santa Ana, California, 1999).

Stewart, George R. *Donner Pass.* (Lane Books, Menlo Par, California, 1964).

Stewart, George R. *The California Trail: An Epic with Many Heroes.* (University of Nebraska Press, Lincoln & London, 1962).

Stewart, George R. *Ordeal by Hunger: The Story of the Donner Party.* (Houghton Mifflin Company, Boston & New York, 1936).

Sutter, John A. *The Sutter Family and the Origins of Gold-Rush Sacramento.* (University of Oklahoma Press, Norman, 1943 and 2002).

Thornton, J. Quinn. *Camp of Death: The Donner Party Mountain Camp 1846-47.* (Outbooks, Inc., Golden, Colorado, 1986).

Unruh, John, D. Jr. *The Plains Across: The Overland Emigrants and the Trans-Mississippi West, 1840-60.* (University of Illinois Pres, Urbana and Chicago, 1979 & 1993).

Walker,Dale, L. *Bear Flag Rising: The Conquest of California, 1846.* (Tom Doherty Associates Book, New York, N.Y. 1999).

WEBSITES

www.utahcrossroads.org/DonnerParty — Kristin Johnson's *New Light on the Donner Party* website is the best and most comprehensive Internet source for solid information on this topic. Johnson is an award-winning author and librarian at Salt Lake Community College.

www.donnerpartydiary.com — Dan Rosen's excellent website contains an abundance of informative content with maps, photos and links to relevant source material. Rosen is an amateur historian with a passion for chronicling the Donner Party story.

www.thestormking.com — Mark McLaughlin's website contains stories and updated information regarding the latest archaeology and research projects associated with the Donner Party encampment sites. McLaughlin is a weather historian with a focus on Nevada, California and Sierra Nevada climatology.

About the Author

Weather historian Mark McLaughlin is an award-winning, nationally published author and photographer with five books and than 500 articles in print. Mark was educated as an historian and cultural geographer at the University of Nevada, Reno, and his work appears regularly in California and Nevada media; he has received the Nevada State Press award five times. Mark frequently writes historical articles for such magazines as *Sierra Heritage*, *Wild West*, *Nevada*, and *Weatherwise*. His work has also been published in the *Reno News & Review*, *Issues in Science & Technology*, and the Grolier Educational *Science Annual* encyclopedia.

A professional and popular lecturer who has lived near North Lake Tahoe since 1978, McLaughlin teaches Sierra Nevada history using dramatic stories, slide shows and field trips. He is also a frequent guest on National Public Radio and has twice consulted for *The History Channel*.

McLaughlin's first two books, *Sierra Stories: True Tales of Tahoe*, Volumes 1 & 2 are regional bestsellers, and his entertaining publication, *Western Train Adventures: The Good, the Bad & the Ugly*, won the Silver Award at the 2003 Northern California Publishers and Authors annual awards gala.

BOOKS BY MARK McLAUGHLIN

Sierra Stories: True Tales of Tahoe — Volumes 1 & 2
Western Train Adventures: The Good, the Bad & the Ugly
Turning the Corner: Energy Solutions for the 21ˢᵗ Century

For more information about Mark McLaughlin's books, photographs, and his extensive work as a weather historian for Nevada, California, and the Sierra Nevada, visit his website:
<www.MicMacMedia.com>